Write Better Stories and Essays:

Topics and Techniques to Improve Writing Skills for Students in Grades 3 Through 5

Write Better Stories and Essays: Topics and Techniques to Improve Writing Skills for Students in Grades 3 Through 5

Contributing Editor And Author	- George Smith
Contributing Editor	- Marisa Adams
Contributing Student Authors	- Emily Adams
	- Vibhu M. Krishnaswamy
	- McKinlea Poland
	- Jasmine Brunton
Designer	- Sowmya R

ISBN-10: 194048474X
ISBN-13: 978-1-940484-74-7

Printed in the United States of America

For permissions and additional information contact us

Lumos Information Services, LLC
PO Box 1575, Piscataway, NJ 08855-1575
http:/www.lumoslearning.com

Email: support@lumoslearning.com
Tel: (888) 408-1689
Fax: (866)283-6471

ABOUT THE AUTHOR

George Smith, a children's book author and publisher, has been conducting writing workshops at schools since 2004. He is passionate about helping young writers turn their creative story ideas to captivating stories that others would enjoy reading. He has authored two children's books, a marine life guide book for science teachers and functioned as an editor for several publications. He lives in Lakewood, New Jersey and loves to travel.

Table of Contents

Explanatory

INTRODUCTION

The objective of this workbook is to improve the essay and story writing skills of students in grades 3 through 5:

- by providing information about selected ELA-Literacy writing standards in the Text Types and Purposes category of the Common Core State Standards program.
- by providing examples and critiques of actual essays and stories written to meet the requirements of these standards.
- by providing additional explanations and guidance about various writing techniques.
- by explaining how to grow a story idea into a full length story.

The names, descriptions and numbers of all ELA-Literacy Text Types and Purposes standards selected for publication in this workbook are listed. Matched with each ELA-Literacy standard are **stories or essays written mostly by students in grades 3 through 5.**

Student Exercises

After each story or essay, space is provided for the students to correct and comment on what they read. This will give students the opportunity to critique, identify errors, and apply best practices to improve essays written by others.

Teachers can assign additional exercises to meet the needs of individual classrooms and students. We have suggested a few topics in each category and teachers can modify them or propose their own topic.

Teacher Guidebook

The teacher guidebook for this book includes detailed corrections, critiques and comments for the student written essays and stories. The objective of the Lumos editors' comments is to evaluate how the essay or story matches up to the requirements of the applicable standard(s), and to suggest changes where it does not match up or does not meet other writing standards.

We hope that your student will enjoy using this workbook and that its use will improve your student's writing skills.

How Teachers and Parents Can Use This Workbook

1. Identifying spelling, grammar and other errors

Following every story or essay is a Corrections and Comments section with blank lines for students to write their comments. You can challenge your student(s) to read each story or essay and look for spelling, capitalization and other grammatical errors as well as redundant text, excessive wordiness, inferior choice of words, phrases or sentences, lack of agreement between nouns and verbs or nouns and personal pronouns, inconsistent formatting (such as for numbers), or essential information that is missing.

When your student has completed his/her analysis of errors or imperfections in the story or essay, you can compare your student's results with those of the Lumos editors which are presented in an edited version of the story or essay.

2. Identifying the characteristics of the six Text Types and Purposes

This workbook clearly defines each of the six Text Types and provides stories and essays as examples of writing that aims to meet the standards of each Text Type. It can be used to teach your students the differences between each Text Type and what requirements should be met when they write essays and stories intended to meet the standards for each Text Type.

3. At the end of each Text Type section there are suggestions for story ideas from which your students can select a topic to write about.

Author's Point of View, Text Types and Purposes and Transitions

Author's Point of View

As an author, you need to decide from which point of view you are writing to the reader: first person, second person or third person. Each of these is defined below, and suggestions for which person to use are included in each text type.

First person: The author is the one telling the story to the reader. The story may be about a topic the author has actually experienced or seen (nonfiction), or a topic that the author made-up (fiction). When writing in the first person, the author does not give directions or instructions to the reader. Also, the author uses the personal pronouns I, we, me, us, my, mine, our or ours in the essay.

Second person: The author is addressing the reader, giving instructions or suggestions for the reader to follow. The author will use the personal pronouns you or yours in the essay.

Third person: The author is not a character in the story, but is a narrator telling the story as an outside observer. The narrator may or may not know all the thoughts and feelings of one or more characters in the story. The author will use the personal pronouns he, she, it, him, his, her, hers, it or its in the essay.

Text Types and Purposes

The terms **Text Types and Purposes** are used in the Common Core State Standards to describe four major categories of essay and story writing: Argument, Informative, Explanatory, and Narrative.

In this workbook, we have added the text type "Opinion" because it is different from the text type "Argument" (although they are closely related) and we have divided the "Narrative" text type into "Narrative Fiction" and "Narrative Nonfiction" because there is a significant difference between the two that students should be aware of.

In this workbook are essays and stories written to meet the Common Core standards for each text type. Each essay or story is presented individually, followed by a Corrections and Comments section with blank lines for students to write their own notes, suggestions or corrections that apply to the story.

Following the first presentation of the essay or story is a second presentation of the same essay or story, in a two column format. The first (Story) column contains the story or essay, and also comments, suggestions or corrections from the Lumos editors. The second column (Comments) lists the Common Core standards that apply to the text type under which the essay or story is written, with examples from the essay or story that meet the requirements of the standard. This column may also have critiques and suggestions for improvement from the Lumos editors if something in the essay or story does not meet the standard.

Text Type and Purpose 1: Narrative Fiction

Narrative Fiction: A story or account of events or experiences that did not actually occur; that are made-up by the author.
Point of view: You normally write narrative fiction stories in the first or third person.

Text Type and Purpose 2: Narrative Nonfiction

Narrative Nonfiction: A story or account of events or experiences that are true, that is, that actually occurred.
Point of view: You normally write narrative nonfiction stories in the first person or third person.

Text Type and Purpose 3: Opinion

Opinion: A belief or judgment about which the believer is not absolutely certain or positive.

You can write an opinion from your point of view (first person) or from someone else's point of view (third person). You should include a clear statement of the opinion and the reasons why you have the opinion being expressed. You can also choose to compare your opinion to someone else's opinion. The Common Core standards for writing an opinion are listed in the Comments column of each essay.

Text Type and Purpose 4: Argument

Argument: A discussion in which differences in opinions (different points of view) are presented. A debate. More forceful than an opinion. More demanding of a justification, because an argument involves two or more differences of opinion competing with each other to try and prove which point of view is more correct and/or to convince an audience to accept an argument. The word "argument" as used in this document means a discussion, not an emotion such as anger.

You can present arguments in favor of an issue, opposed to an issue, or both (include opposite points of view on an issue). You can write an argument essay in the first, second or third person. If you write in the second person, your argument is directed at the reader personally in order to convince him or her to accept your argument.

An argument essay must follow this format to meet the Common Core standards:

- clearly explain the issue
- clearly explain your position on the issue
- provide facts or opinions to support your position. You can choose to comment on an opposing position as well, if it helps support your argument.
- provide a concluding statement, which can be a summary of the position you have taken and/or recommendations for action your audience can take.

Text Type and Purpose 5: Informative

Informative: Serving to inform or educate or instruct by giving information about a topic.

Give information about a topic. Examples: The lifecycle of a butterfly, the history of your town, an event you attended or witnessed (a school play, a sports contest, a destructive storm). You do not have to make a judgment or convince someone to accept your point of view (as in an Opinion/Argument essay) or explain how something works (as in an Explanatory essay). You normally write informative essays in the first or third person.

Text Type and Purpose 6: Explanatory

Explanatory: Serving to explain or clarify by giving information about a topic.

Explain how to perform or accomplish a process or task or procedure or how to resolve a problem or overcome an obstacle.

Examples: how to select a video game or clothes for school or a skateboard; how to get elected class president; how to get a specific food item added to the cafeteria menu; how to create and carry out a project that will help people less fortunate than you and that will involve your classmates.
You normally write explanatory essays in the second person.

Transitions[1]

As used in writing, transitions refer to words and phrases that link parts of a story together. There are several kinds of transitions, and they are listed below with some examples. In the stories in this workbook, the author will identify some transitions by type.

Addition: indicates that more information relating to a topic in the story will follow.
    Examples: "furthermore," "next."
Time: indicates a period of time over which an event in a story will occur.
    Examples: "immediately," "in the meantime," "after," "while," "next," "then."
Place: Indicates a location.
    Examples: "here," "nearby," "above."
Exemplification or Illustration: Examples: "for instance," "specifically," "for example."
Comparison: a comparison of like or similar events or ideas.
    Examples: "likewise," "similarly," "in the same way."
Contrast: a comparison to show the differences between events or ideas.
    Examples: "however," "on the other hand," "but," "otherwise."
Clarification: an explanation of an event or idea that follows a previous explanation except that this one uses different words.
    Examples: """in other words," "to explain," "to clarify."

Cause: an explanation of the reason an event or idea happened.

Examples: "because," "since," "on account of."

Effect: the result that follows when an event or idea happens or is proposed.

Examples: "therefore," "consequently," "as a result."

Purpose: the reason for an event happening or for an idea being proposed.

Examples: "in order that," "so that," "for this purpose."

Qualification: describes the frequency or likelihood that an event or idea or requirement (such as a skill) will occur or must be met in order for a certain result to take place.

Examples: "almost," "never," "frequently," "maybe."

Intensification: describes the action a writer can take to make an event or idea more dramatic, more intense in feeling, in force or earnestness.

Examples: "without doubt," "surely," "yes," "no," "certainly."

Concession: something given up, conceded or yielded by a character in a story.

Examples: "granted, I recognize that you have a right to…"; "I would normally insist on this, but under the circumstances…."

Summary: to restate the main points or events in an argument or proposal of an idea, usually in a brief, concise manner.

Examples: "to summarize," "in sum," "in short," "in brief."

Conclusion: the ending of any written text type. It may be the ending of a story, it may present a settlement of a conflict, and it may present the author's opinion on an issue and the author's recommendation.

Examples: "in conclusion," "finally," "in closing."

[1]College of Letters and Science. 8/29/2014. The Writer's Handbook: Transitional Words and Phrases. University of Wisconsin, Madison, Wisconsin

Growing A Story Idea into a Full Length Story

You are planning to write a story. The first step is **choosing a topic.** If I asked you to list all of the topics that you could write a story about, I imagine your list would be very long. Am I right? It's easy to choose a topic to write about, isn't it?

Once you decide on your topic, it will help if you write an outline, usually only a few sentences long, about the topic. Your outline should tell what events and actions you will include in your story, who the main characters are, where your story takes place and when it takes place. This outline is your **story idea**.

Here are the six sentences that make up the story idea for a book by author George Smith titled "The Journey of the Little Red Boat":

1. **A girl named Grace is visiting her grandfather and grandmother during the summer at their house on an island in a river in Maine.**
2. **When looking out her bedroom window one morning, Grace sees an empty red boat drifting into view on the river, heading for their dock.**
3. **She awakens her grandfather and they run to the dock, where he catches the boat as it drifts by and ties it to the dock.**
4. **The next day they have to leave Maine for home, so they tow the red boat to the town dock, tie it up and leave it there.**
5. **They stop at the local post office, attach a "Boat Found" sign to the bulletin board, and leave for home.**
6. **Winter and spring come and go and no one claims the boat. So the grandfather gives the boat to a friend who needs one, and hardly ever sees the boat again.**

While it's usually easy to choose a topic and write a story idea, it is harder to grow this story idea from a few sentences or paragraphs into a full length story of many paragraphs and many pages. This chapter will share with you:

- The most important elements (parts) that make up a story.
- Steps you can use to grow your story idea from the outline to a full length story.

Building a Story

It will help you understand what elements are if we compare building a story to building a house.

	Building a House	Building a Story
1.	Start with the foundation (it may be a basement or a slab).	Start with choosing your topic
2.	Add a framework of supports for walls, floors, ceilings, roof and window openings.	Create an outline of your story idea.
3.	Add utilities such as plumbing, heating air conditioning and electrical wiring and outlets to the framework.	Look at each sentence in your story idea outline and decide which element it belongs under. We will explain what elements are later in this chapter, but for now, here are the three basic elements in a story: **plot, characters and setting.** You will most likely have at least one idea from your outline that belongs under each element. If an element that you think is important does not have an idea under it, you should add a new idea to your outline that belongs under that element.
4.	Add solid walls, floors, ceilings, a roof and windows to the framework.	Grow your story by adding more details and descriptions to each sentence in your story idea. Because you have now assigned each story idea to one or more story elements, expanding each story idea results in expanding each element that makes up the story. We will show you several ways to expand each element later in this chapter.
5.	Add trimmings such as molding, cabinets and shutters.	Add extras such as photos, diagrams, charts, a table of contents and front and back cover designs to your story.
6.	Sell the house and let the buyer's family move in and enjoy living there.	Publish your story so people can enjoy reading it.

The Elements (Parts) Of a Story

1. Plot

The plot is the main story of a literary work[1]. There can be more than one plot in a story, and there can be one or more secondary (less important) plots (also called subplots). In this chapter, we will present details of a story with one plot and one subplot.

Looking at the story idea for "The Journey of the Little Red Boat," we can see that the plot (main story) is focused on the little red boat. All of the events that take place and all of the actions by the characters and the location (setting) are caused by or directed at the little red boat.

[1] *Random House Webster's College Dictionary*, 1992, Random House Inc., New York.

2. Character(s)

The actions and thoughts and emotions of the main (major) character(s) have the most influence, are the most important, to the plot. There may be other less important characters (known as minor or secondary characters) in the story, but they will have less influence on the plot.

Looking at the story idea for "The Journey of the Little Red Boat," we see four characters: a young girl named Grace, her grandmother and grandfather and the little red boat (remember that characters do not have to be human or even real).

The author will determine if each character is a major character or a minor character by the amount of influence he/she allows the character to have on the plot. Even though the story has not been fully written when the story idea outline is written, it seems obvious at this point that the red boat and Grace will be main characters.

3. Setting(s)

The setting(s) for a story are the location(s) and/or time period(s) at or in which the story takes place. There can be more than one setting and more than one time period in the same story.

Looking at the story idea for "The Journey of the Little Red Boat," we can see that the initial setting is a house on an island in a river in Maine, in the summer time period.

Because the word "journey" is in the title, it seems obvious that the setting will change during the journey; maybe the time period (hours or days) will change also.

Story Idea	Element
1.1 A girl named Grace is visiting her grandfather and grandmother 1.2. Grace, grandfather and grandmother 1.3. during the summer 1.4. at their house on an island in a river in Maine.	1.1 Plot 1.2. Characters 1.3. Time Setting 1.4. Place Setting
2. While sitting on the deck, Grace and her grandfather see an empty red boat drifting into view on the river.	2. Plot
3. They run to the dock, he catches the boat as it drifts by and ties it to the dock.	3. Plot
4.1 The next day they have to leave Maine for home, 4.2 so they tow the red boat to the town dock, tie it up and leave it there.	4.1 Plot, Time Setting change 4.2 Plot, Place Setting change
5.1 They stop at the local post office, attach a "Boat Found" sign to the bulletin board, 5.2 and leave for home.	5.1 Plot, Place Setting change 5.2 Plot, Place Setting change
6.1 Winter and spring come and go and no one claims the boat. 6.2 So the grandfather's brother, who lives in Maine, gives the boat to a friend who needs one, and they never see the boat again.	6.1 Plot, Time Setting change 6.2 Plot, Place Setting change

Growing Your Story

In the *Building a Story* section above, we stated that "We will show you several ways to expand each element later in this chapter." There were five steps author Smith used to grow the story idea for "The Journey of the Little Red Boat" from the six sentences in the story idea outline to a full length story with twenty four pages of text and twenty four pages of pictures (48 pages in all). The good news is **that you can use these same five steps to grow your stories, no matter how short or long your stories are.** But before you read about the five steps, why don't you write down as many steps as you can think of that you would use to grow any story you write from a story idea to a full length story?

Author Smith's Steps to Growing Your Story from the Story Idea

1. Plots: Adding events to the existing plot and adding a subplot.
2. Characters: Adding information about the four characters. Adding new characters and information about them. Adding interactions among the characters.
3. Place Setting: Adding descriptions. Adding additional place settings.
4. Time Setting: Adding time periods.
5. Adding graphics

Step 1. Plots

The story idea appears to have only one plot (main story line) and it is all about the boat: the boat drifts to where Grace and her grandparents live, they rescue it, tie it to the public dock and post a Boat Found sign as they leave for home. The plot focuses its words and pictures on the boat; neither Grace nor her grandparents are mentioned or shown in pictures in the first 23 pages.

But then on page 24 the author introduces a subplot. The subplot focuses its words and pictures on Grace and her grandparents through page 27. Then the plot and subplot come together and become one on page 28, when Grace looks out the window early in the morning and sees the boat floating in the water near grandpa's dock. From this point on, the author talks about the boat and Grace and her grandparents.

Mr. Smith also grows his story by adding events to the plot. For example:

- A description of the little red boat's life at its original home, mentioning how it gets towed behind the sailboat when the family takes a sailing trip, and what things it sees from its dock.
- The rainstorm that fills the boat partly with water and breaks its tie line, and the start of its journey downriver as a result.
- Details of the boat's journey downriver – its encounters with a rock, sailboats, seal and cormorant birds.
- How grandpa and Grace clean the boat, use it, meet the owner when he comes to claim it, paint it and add a name to the stern (back) of the boat after the owner gives them the boat.
- How Grace at first and later on with her family come to visit the little red boat and grandma and grandpa each summer, for years.

The author also adds plot twists. A plot twist is an unexpected event that takes place in a plot. The plot twists in this story are: when the family sells the sailboat; when the storm breaks the tie line; when the boat is rejected by the things she meets on her journey downriver; when she is rescued by Grace and grandpa; when the owner gives the boat to Grace and grandpa.

Step 2. Characters

We mentioned earlier that there are four characters mentioned in the Story Idea.
The author grows the story through the characters in many ways.

1. Grandpa is included in many events: running to the dock with Grace and grabbing the boat, emptying the water out, tying the boat to the dock and looking for the owner's name; calling people to find the boat's owner; helping Grace clean the boat and joining her in the boat to fish and pick flowers for grandma; answering the phone when the owner calls and inviting him to come and get his boat; going to the dock with Grace to meet the owner; helping Grace paint the boat when the owner gives it to them; storing the boat in the barn for the winter.

2. The author tells the reader why Grace is at her grandparents' house, and what she enjoys doing when she is there.

3. The author describes Grace's emotions in several situations: excited (when she sees the boat; when grandpa catches it; when the owner gives the boat to Grace and grandpa); affectionate (she hugs the boat each morning and evening; she visits the boat each summer for years); anxious (when she is waiting for the owner's decision on what to do with the boat); happy (when she and grandpa use the boat to go fishing or pick flowers)

4. The author adds other characters to the story: the owner of the boat, the owner's sailboat, a talking rock, talking sailboats, a talking seal, cormorant birds and blue birds, an old boat and a raccoon.

5. The author adds interest and dialogue to the story through a writing technique called "personification." Personification means giving human abilities to something that is not human. In this story, the author gives the little red boat the ability to talk and have feelings He describes the little red boat's emotions in several situations: happy (when she is at her original home and takes trips tied behind the sailboat; when Grace and grandpa rescue her; when the owner gives them the boat; when Grace hugs her; when she is in the barn for the winter and has a boat and other animals to talk with); sad (when the owner sells the sailboat, which is the red boat's best friend; when the rock and sailboats tell her to go away, the seal does not stay with her and the cormorants fly away); scared (when the storm breaks her rope and she drifts down the river and thinks she will drift all the way to the ocean and sink before anyone finds her).

6. The author also gives other characters the ability to talk and have feelings, such as the rock, sailboats, seal, birds, raccoon and an old boat.

7. The author also tells the reader about what the little red boat, Grace and the boat's owner are thinking to themselves and not sharing with the other characters. For example: when the owner comes to claim his boat, both Grace, the boat and the owner have private thoughts that only they and you, the reader, know about. Adding a character's private thoughts adds to the length of the story and makes the reader feel like they are included in the story.

Step 3. Place Setting

Describing the setting can help the reader understand events in a story, and should complement the plot and personalities and actions of the characters and add to the length of the story. In this story, the author describes the setting as a salt water river in Maine. Typical of salt water rivers is that they have a current (tide), and in this story, the tide moves the boat downstream on its journey. Also, the animals and objects that the boat meets are found in Maine (seals and cormorants, for example). Also, Maine has snow, sleet and rain, which are the reasons that the boat is put in the barn for shelter, a barn where all the inhabitants have conversations.

Step 4. Time Setting

The time period for this story could be any recent time in which the clothes that Grace, her grandparents and the owner are wearing are typical. Within the story, the author does not tell how old the boat is or how long it was at its original home, or how long it took to complete its journey down the river, or exactly how many year's grandpa and grandma owned the boat and Grace came to visit the boat. These time periods are not important to the story.

The author does mention that while the boat was at her grandparents' house, Grace grew up and went to high school and then college and then had her own family. Also, during the boat's journey downriver, the time changes from daylight to nighttime to daylight again.

Step 5. Adding graphics

By graphics we mean photos and illustrations. Graphics can make a story more interesting, and they add length to a story. By including illustrations in this story, the author almost doubled the length of the story.

In a picture book, photographs and illustrations are often used to help describe the setting because then the author does not have to provide as much written detail; the reader can look at the photos and illustrations and learn many details that way (for example, how a character looks or is dressed; what a building or scenic view or street looks like).

Other Information

The author decided not to include some information that was in the story idea.
The information left out of the story is:

- The next day they have to leave Maine for home, so they tow the red boat to the town dock, tie it up and leave it there.
- They stop at the local post office, attach a "Boat Found" sign to the bulletin board, and leave for home.
- Winter and spring come and go and no one claims the boat. So the grandfather gives the boat to a friend who needs one, and hardly ever sees the boat again.

Conclusion

We hope that you have enjoyed reading this chapter. We hope that you will use the information in this chapter to make your stories longer and more interesting.

EXERCISES: 

Below are three story ideas. Read each story idea and expand each using the four ways to expand a story described above in this chapter.

Story Idea #1: A Boat And Its Journey

Setting: a tidal river in the state of Maine
This story idea is about a small rowboat that is owned by a family and is tied to their dock.

After several days of rain, she fills with water and becomes so heavy that the wind and tide combine to snap her mooring line. She drifts down the tidal river, and as she drifts, she encounters various living and nonliving things typically found on a tidal river in Maine. Finally, she drifts into a cove on whose shore sits a house. A child of about 11 years old looks out the window of the house and sees the boat drifting toward their dock. Her family does not own a boat.

STUDENTS' WRITING ASSIGNMENT:

1. Write sentences or phrases describing how you would expand this story idea to a multi page story that would appeal to elementary school students. Assume this will be a picture book with story text. Use each of the four ways to expand a story that were described above in this chapter. You don't have to actually write the expanded story (unless you want to); you just have to describe the ideas you have for expanding the story.

2. Include in the story at least one example of a marine life creature that would inhabit a tidal river in Maine, and explain how you were able to determine that this creature would live there.

3. Which character or characters would tell the story and why did you choose them?

4. What title and subtitle (a subtitle is a short phrase that adds more detail to the actual title) would you give the story?

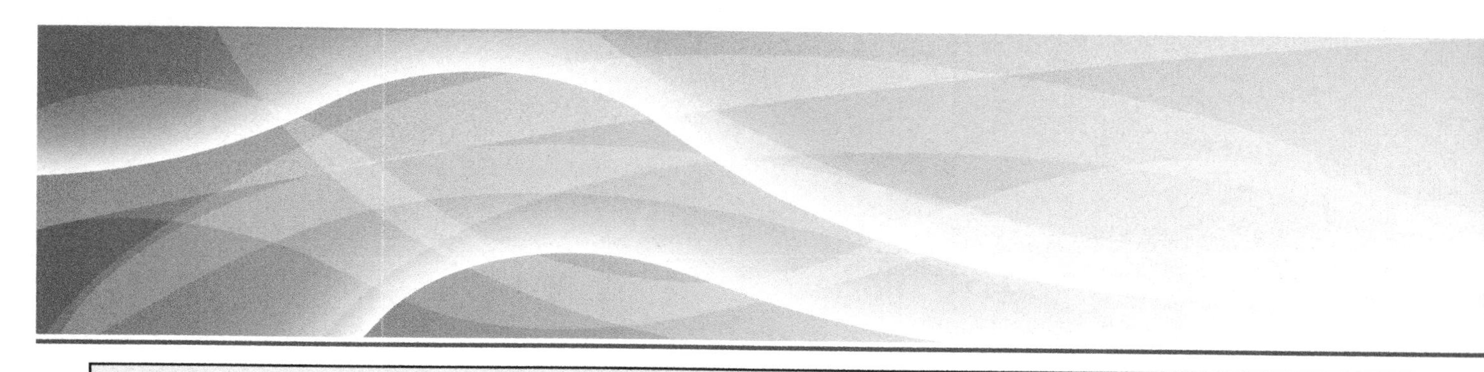

Story Idea #2: An Amazing Chicken

<u>Setting</u>: *The area of the United States known as the Far West (includes states like Colorado, Arizona, New Mexico).*

A family of two parents and four children live in the Far West, on a two acre ranchette (a ranchette is a small ranch – just a couple of acres). They own a pig, several horses and ponies, goats, dogs, cockatoo birds, a rabbit and several hens. The family notices that one of the hens is very intelligent and friendly, and interacts with the other animals and with the family members. Because of these character traits, they give her a special name. They become very fond of her, and brag about her to all their friends.

<u>STUDENTS' WRITING ASSIGNMENT:</u>

1. Write sentences or phrases describing how you would expand this story idea to a multipage story that would appeal to <u>readers in grades three to five</u>. You can assume this will have photographs with story text.

Use each of the four ways to expand a story that were described in this chapter. You don't have to actually write the expanded story (unless you want to); you just have to describe the ideas you have for expanding the story.

2. Who would you select to tell the story and why?

3. What title and subtitle (a subtitle is a short phrase that adds more detail to the actual title) would you give the story?

Story Idea #3: The Boy From Africa

Settings: A poor country in Africa and a school and community in the U.S.

You are a children's book author and you are looking for a new subject to write a book about. In the newspaper, you read an article about a teacher in an American school where many students are refugees from Liberia, an African country that has been involved in a civil war. This teacher is so moved by the sad stories that she hears from her students that she is determined to do something to help those left behind in the African country. Included in ways she is willing to help is the option of adopting an African child who is of elementary school age, since she does not have children of her own.

STUDENTS' WRITING ASSIGNMENT:

1. Write sentences or phrases describing how you would expand this story idea to a multipage story that would appeal to readers in grades three to five. You can assume this will be a picture book with story text.

Use each of the four ways to expand a story that were described in this chapter. You don't have to actually write the expanded story (unless you want to); you just have to describe the ideas you have for expanding the story

The Teacher adopts four kids from Liberia due to the fact that she wants to help the kids that were left behind. She continue's too feed and teach these young children. Then The Teacher decides to work for a school that teaches refugees from Liberia. She brings food for the kids every morning and makes the kids feel at home because the kids parents are dead. She Signs up to work for a homeless shelter that has taken care of the families.

F.Q 02/16/22

2. Explain how you would find out information about life in an African village in Liberia, to use in the story.

I would do my research on the internet because it has all the information I could possibly need.

3. Who would you select to tell the story and why?

My mom so she can finally be proud of me

4. What title and subtitle (a subtitle is a short phrase that adds more detail to the actual title) would you give the story?

The Teacher who cares. It suits my story perfectly.

Text Types and Purposes Category: Narrative Fiction

Standard: CCSS.ELA-Literacy.W.5.3

Narrative Fiction: A story or account of events or experiences that did not actually occur; that are made-up by the author. Point of view: You normally write narrative fiction stories in the first or third person.

Title: Inside a Snow Globe by McKinlea Poland

1. How would you feel if you were in a snow globe?
   I got in there by disturbing an evil unicorn.
   It feels freezing in there, but I have a house with a fire in it.
   It feels freezing because there is white snow.
5. There is people in there so I play with toys and my pet unicorn.
   I would ice skate on a frozen lake. I would build a snowman too.
   I love it in there so I stayed in there forever.
   It was amazing being inside a snow globe.

Corrections and Comments

Student Name:	**Date:**
Example: Line #2 → I got in ~~there~~ [***one***] by disturbing an evil unicorn.	
Note: “One” is a more precise reference to a snow globe than “there.”	

Edited Version: Inside a Snow Globe by McKinlea Poland

STORY	COMMENTS
How would you feel if you were in a snow globe? I got in ~~there~~ [***one***] by disturbing an evil unicorn. *[Editor's Note: "One" is a more precise reference to a snow globe than "there."]*	1. **This story clearly states a situation.** "How would you feel if you were in a snow globe? I got in one by disturbing an evil unicorn." *CCSS ELA-Literacy.W.5.3.a* 2. **It is obvious that there is a narrator** (who happens to be the author) and she tells the story in the first person (a story written in the first person uses the pronouns "my", "I", "we.") *CCSS ELA-Literacy.W.5.3.a* 3. **The sequence of events unfolds naturally, in a time sequence.** "I got in one…" followed by "…I stayed in there forever." *CCSS ELA-Literacy.W.5.3.a*
It feels freezing in ~~there~~ [***here***], but I have a house with a fire in it. *[Editor's Note: The author writes that she got into the snow globe, so it is more logical to write "It feels freezing in here…." instead of "It feels freezing in there…"]*	4. **Narrative techniques used:** **Descriptions.** "It feels freezing in the snow globe, but I have a house with a fire in it."; "…there is white snow. There are people in there so I play with toys and my pet unicorn. I would ice skate on a frozen lake. I would build a snowman too."

STORY	COMMENTS
It feels freezing in ~~there~~ [***here***] because there is white snow. There ~~is~~ [***are***] people in ~~there~~ [***here***] so I play with toys and my pet unicorn. *[Editor's Note: Because the author is in the snow globe, it is more logical to write "There are people in here…" instead of "There are people in there…"]*	**Bonding the reader with the author.** "How would you feel if you were in a snow globe?" Asking the reader a question is a good technique because it causes the reader to think about the answer to the author's question; it strengthens the bond between author and reader. *CCSS ELA-Literacy.W.5.3.b* **5. Responses of characters to situations.** "I got in one by disturbing an evil unicorn."; "It feels freezing in the snow globe…"; "There are people in there so I play with toys and my pet unicorn."; "I love it in there…" *CCSS ELA-Literacy.W.5.3.b*
I ~~would~~ [***will***] ice skate on a frozen lake. I ~~would~~ [***will***] build a snowman too. *[Editor's Note: Because the author is in the snow globe, change "would" to "will"]*	**6. Concrete words, sensory details.** "It feels freezing in the snow globe…"; "I love it in there" *CCSS ELA-Literacy.W.5.3.d*
I love it in ~~there~~ [***here***] so I stayed in ~~there~~ [***here***] forever. *[Editor's Note: The same reasoning from the note above applies to this sentence.]*	**7. Conclusion**. "I love it in there so I stayed in there forever. It was amazing being inside a snow globe." *CCSS ELA-Literacy.W.5.3.e*

STORY	COMMENTS
It ~~was~~ [***is***] amazing being inside a snow globe. *[Editor's Note: Replace "was" with "is" because the author is still in there.]*	**8. Not a logical agreement between statements.** How can the unicorn that let the author into the snow globe be evil if the author says "I love it in here?" Suggest the author delete the word "evil" and have the unicorn also be the author's pet unicorn inside the snow globe.

Title: The Cloud Academy by Vibhu M. Krishnaswamy

1. Sean lived in a small farming town called Baboville. He was in fifth grade and was known for his mischievous behavior. He was terrible at studies!

2. It was the first Monday in April. Sean went to school as usual, but his report card awaited him. His teachers were very unhappy with his grades and had made remarks on the report card that he is naughty and inattentive in class. He was very frustrated with the school work; He was afraid to show his parents the report card.

3. After school he told his teacher that he had to rehearse for the school play and stayed back hoping to decrease the chances of getting yelled at home. While waiting for the after school bus, he kept rubbing his eyes to fight his frustration and the Spring allergies. Suddenly he saw an eyelash on his finger. His friend Nina excitedly said, "Hi, that's a wish!" She asked him to wish for something he really wanted. Sean thought for a moment and whispered, """I wish I didn't have to come to this pesky school with so many rules, but could go somewhere where I could have fun and learn".

4. He reached home and saw that his mom was busy helping his dad pack. That night his dad was leaving for Zurich for a business meeting. He was kind of relieved that his parents were busy and did not ask much about the school. It was dinner time; his mom had made his favorite, the green bean casserole! While eating dinner he watched the Chile COPA America 2015 Finals match. Just before finishing dinner Sean's mom asked, "Sean, did you get your report card today?" Sean's heart started beating really fast! He composed himself and said, "No, Mom, apparently there was a delay and we are likely to get

our cards next week!" He went to the airport with his mom to drop his dad off at the airport. All evening Sean kept to himself and was feeling really guilty about his lies.

5. The next morning he got up normally and got ready for school. After he got ready, he went to get his back-pack. He could not find his regular back-pack. Surprisingly there was a new fluorescent green school bag in his room. He didn't have the time to investigate where it came from, but happily packed his books and lunch in his newly found bag. He wished his mom good bye and started walking toward the bus stop.

6. He saw the bus fast approaching his stop and started running to catch the bus. But something really weird started happening; he felt very light and started to gently float! He screamed impatiently and started moving his hands. But, as soon as he spread his hands, he started moving up faster instead of landing back on the ground. Everything below him started to look smaller. His house started to look like a tiny toy! He could see his mom, but she could not hear his scream!

7. His ascent did not stop. After a few minutes, he found himself inside a huge cloud. The fluffy cloud looked kind of strange and felt cool. After that brief moment in the cloud, he emerged back into the open sky, but his beating of hands or legs didn't make any difference. His body kept moving up as if someone was guiding it to a destination.

8. As he was moving up without control he was really scared and confused. Suddenly, Sean started hearing faint voices and he could tell that there were children. Very quickly he entered into a large cloud and found himself in the middle of a huge building with kids playing and talking. He did not know what to do. Now, his flight also had stopped. He started to look around. In the middle of the cloud there were

buildings and a playground. There was something that looked like a stadium too. Kids that were playing looked very excited and happy. One of them even waved at Sean, but he was too overwhelmed to re spond.

9. Sean felt a tap on his back. He was a little startled and turned around. A boy about his height introduced himself "Hi Sean, I am Alby! Welcome to Cloud Academy!" Sean responded back with a Hi and was really happy that he could find another person to talk to. He had so many questions. Alby read his mind "Sean I know you must be wondering about what is happening and why you are here. You were one of the students our committee picked to learn at our school. We need teammates like you that are curious and good at figuring things out". Sean looked at him with more questions, but allowed Alby to continue. "I am the head boy for this week and your guide. I'll help you get started here. We don't have much time today to go over all your questions, but I need you to pick a topic for today and I'll take you to that team. Here are 7 topics that other students are exploring today." He pulled out a list that had the following topics:
   How to make kites
   How to solve a Rubik's Cube
   How to build a castle
   How to ride a unicycle
   What causes typhoons in China
   Why does Asian music sound so different compared to pop
   How to make a Frittata

10. Sean thought the topics were cool, but picked How to solve a Rubik's Cube. He knew how to solve one face and was eager to figure out the rest. Alby quickly walked him toward a group of kids that were excitedly working with their Cubes. Alby said with a smile, "Hi guys, this is Sean our new team member. He wants to join your group and figure out the Rubik's Cube!"

Other kids said "Hi" and made room for him. One of the boys offered him a Cube and said, "This is yours. Twirl it dude!"

Sean quickly solved the first face and the one of the boys said, "That is cool. Can you teach me"? Sean slowly walked him through the steps. Solving the second layer was a piece of cake for two other kids, but Sean was stuck. One of the boys, that looked a little older, walked up to Sean and gave him some pointers. Sean kept watching him and then tried on his own. It didn't work at first, but after about half hour, Sean got it. He was so happy. He walked up to that kid that helped him and said, "Thank you! I got the second layer". He suddenly heard a bell and his new friends started packing their bags.

11. Alby came running to him and said, "Sean it's time to go home. I have programmed your bag for your return flight. By the way, you are the team leader tomorrow for a group. You get to pick a topic that you want to explore. Think about it! Bye"

12. The descent back home was exciting, but not scary anymore. All Sean could think about was "What should I explore tomorrow?"

Corrections and Comments

Student Name:	**Date:**
Example: Paragraph #1 → Sean lived in a small farming town called Baboville. He was in fifth grade	
and was known for his mischievous behavior.	
Note: The author does not give examples of Sean's mischievous behavior in the story, so this reference can	
be deleted.	

Edited Version: The Cloud Academy by Vibhu M. Krishnaswamy

STORY	COMMENTS
Sean lived in a small farming town called Baboville. He was in fifth grade and was known for his mischievous behavior. *[Editor's Note: The author does not give examples of Sean's mischievous behavior in the story, so this reference can be deleted."]*	**1. This story clearly states a situation.** "He was in fifth grade and …"; "He got poor grades at school." "Because he was afraid to show his parents the report card…" "Surprisingly there was a new fluorescent green school bag in his room." "But something really weird started happening; he felt very light and started to gently float!" "Suddenly, Sean started hearing faint voices which he recognized were from children." *CCSS ELA-Literacy.W.5.3.a*
~~He was terrible at studies!~~ ***[He got poor grades at school.]*** *[Editor's Note: "terrible" is too general; "poor grades" is more specific.]*	**2. It is obvious that there is a narrator** (who happens to be the author) and he tells the story in the third person (a story written in the third person uses the pronouns "he", "she", "it"). *CCSS ELA-Literacy.W.5.3.a*
It was the first Monday in April, ~~Sean went to school as usual, but his report card awaited him.~~ [***and report cards were handed out***]. ~~His teachers were very unhappy with his grades and had made remarks on the report card~~ His teachers [***commented on his report card that they were very unhappy with his low grades and***] that he is naughty and ~~un [~~*in*]attentive in class. *[Editor's Note: The rewritten sentences say the same things with fewer words.].*	**3. The sequence of events unfolds naturally, in a time sequence.** The story begins with Sean going to school, then going home, then the next day finding the new bag, then being transported to the clouds and the Cloud Academy then coming back home. *CCSS ELA-Literacy.W.5.3.a*

STORY	COMMENTS
He was very frustrated with the school work. *[Editor's Note: Author should explain why he was frustrated – was he bored? Was the work too hard?]* [***Because***] ~~H~~ [***h***]e was afraid to show his parents the report card, [***he***] ~~After school he told~~ [***lied to***] his [***homeroom***] teacher that he had to [***stay at school to***] rehearse for the school play. ~~and stayed back hoping to~~ [***He figured that by getting home later, he would***] decrease the chances of getting yelled at ~~home.~~ [***because of his report card***].	**4. The essay uses the narrative technique of responses of characters to situations.** "He was very frustrated with the school work." "Because he was afraid to show his parents the report card…" "Wish for something you really want. Sean thought for a moment and whispered…" "All evening Sean kept to himself and was feeling really guilty about his lies." "He screamed impatiently and started moving his hands." "This lack of control really scared and confused him." *CCSS ELA-Literacy.W.5.3.b and* *CCSS ELA-Literacy.W.5.3.d*
While waiting ~~for the~~ after school [***for the late***] bus, he kept rubbing his eyes to fight his frustration and ~~the~~ his ~~S~~ [***s***]pring allergies. Suddenly he saw an eyelash on his finger. His friend Nina excitedly said, "~~Hi,~~ [***See that eyelash?***] ~~that's a wish!"~~ [***That means good luck.***] ~~She asked him to~~ [***W***]ish for something ~~he~~ [***you***] really want~~ed~~." Sean thought for a moment and whispered, "I wish I didn't have to come to this pesky school with so many rules, but could go somewhere where I could have fun and learn".	**5. Transitional words** *Time transition:* "the first Monday"; "While waiting after school…"; "The next morning…" Cause transition: "Because he was afraid to show his parents the report card…"

STORY	COMMENTS
He reached home and saw that his mom was busy helping his dad pack. That night his dad was leaving for Zurich for a business meeting. He was ~~kind of~~ relieved that his parents were busy and did not ask ~~much~~ anything about the school. It was dinner time; his mom had made his favorite, the green bean casserole! While eating dinner he watched the Chile COPA America 2015 Finals [***soccer***] match. Just before finishing dinner Sean's mom asked, "Sean, did you get your report card today?" Sean's heart started beating really fast! He composed himself and said, "No, Mom, apparently there was a delay and we are likely to get our cards next week!" He went ~~to the airport~~ with his mom to drop his dad off at the airport. All evening Sean kept to himself and was feeling really guilty about his lies. The next morning he got up ~~normally~~ and got ready for school. After he got ready, he went to get his ~~back-pack~~ [***backpack***]. He could not find his regular ~~back-pack~~ [***backpack***.] Surprisingly there was a new fluorescent green school bag in his room. He didn't have the time to investigate where it came from, but happily packed his books and lunch in his newly found bag. ~~He wished his mom good bye~~ [***He said goodbye to his mom***] and started walking toward the bus stop.	

STORY	COMMENTS
He saw the bus fast approaching his stop and started running to catch ~~the bus~~ [***it***]. But something really weird started happening; he felt very light and started to gently float! He screamed impatiently and started moving his hands. But, as soon as he spread his hands, he started ~~moving up~~ [***rising***] faster instead of landing back on the ground. Everything below him started to look smaller. His house started to look like a tiny toy! He could see his mom, but she could not hear his scream! His ascent did not stop. After a few minutes, he found himself inside a huge cloud. The fluffy cloud looked kind of strange and felt cool. After that brief moment in the cloud, he reemerged ~~back~~ into the open sky~~;~~ ~~but his beating of~~ [***and kept moving his***] hands or legs [***but it***] didn't make any difference. His body kept moving up as if someone was guiding it to a destination. [***This lack of control really scared and confused him.***] ~~As he was moving up without control he was really scared and confused.~~ Suddenly, Sean started hearing faint voices ~~and~~ [***which he recognized***] ~~he could tell that there~~ were [***from***] children. Very quickly he entered into a large cloud and found himself in the middle of a huge building with kids playing and talking. He did not know what to do; [***his uncontrolled ascent***] ~~Now, his flight also~~ had stopped. He started to look around ~~In~~	

STORY	COMMENTS
~~the middle of the cloud there were~~ [***and he saw other***] buildings and a playground. There was something that looked like a stadium too. [***The***] ~~K~~ [***k***]ids ~~that~~ [***who***] *[Editor's Note: use "that" when referring to a nonhuman object; use "who" when referring to a human."]* were playing looked very excited and happy. One of them even waved at Sean, but he was too overwhelmed to respond. Sean felt a tap on his back. He was a little startled and turned around. A boy about his height introduced himself. "Hi Sean, I am Alby! Welcome to Cloud Academy!" Sean responded ~~back~~ with a "Hi" and was really happy that he ~~could find~~ [***found***] another person to talk to. He had so many questions. Alby read his mind. "Sean I know you must be wondering about what is happening and why you are here. You were one of the students our committee picked to learn at our school. We need teammates like you ~~that~~ [***who***] are curious and good at figuring things out". ~~Sean looked at him with more questions, but allowed Alby to continue.~~ [***Alby continued:***] "I am the head boy for this week and your guide. I'll help you get started here. We don't have much time today to go over all your questions, but I need you to pick a topic for today and I'll take you to that team. Here are 7 topics that other students are exploring today." He pulled out a list that had the following topics:	

STORY	COMMENTS
How to make kites. How to solve a Rubik's Cube. How to build a castle. How to ride a unicycle. What causes typhoons in China? Why does Asian music sound so different compared to pop? How to make a ~~F~~ [*f*]rittata. Sean thought [***all***] the topics were cool, but picked "How to solve a Rubik's Cube." He knew how to solve one face and was eager to figure out the rest. Alby quickly walked him toward a group of kids ~~that~~ [***who***] were excitedly working with their Cubes. Alby said with a smile, "Hi guys, this is Sean our new team member. He wants to join your group and figure out the Rubik's Cube!" Other kids said "Hi" and made room for him. One of the boys offered him a Cube and said, "This is yours. Twirl it dude!" Sean quickly solved the first face and ~~the~~ one of the boys said, "That is cool. Can you teach me?" Sean slowly walked him through the steps. Solving the second layer was a piece of cake for two other kids, but Sean was stuck. One of the boys, ~~that~~ [***who***] looked a little older, walked up to Sean and gave him some pointers. Sean kept watching him and then tried on his own. It didn't work at first, but after about half [***an***] hour, Sean got it. He was so happy. He walked up to that kid that helped him and said,	

STORY	COMMENTS
"Thank you! I got the second layer". He suddenly heard a bell and his new friends started packing their bags. Alby came running to him and said, "Sean it's time to go home. I have programmed your bag for your return flight. By the way, you are the team leader tomorrow for a group. You get to pick a topic that you want to explore. Think about it! Bye"	
The descent back home was exciting, but not scary anymore. All Sean could think about was "What should I explore tomorrow?" *[Editor's Note: Do not use quotation marks around a character's thoughts; use them only when the character is speaking.]*	**6. Conclusion.** "The descent back home was exciting, but not scary anymore. All Sean could think about was What should I explore tomorrow?" *CCSS ELA-Literacy.W.5.3.e*

Title: Jerry The Unicorn King by McKinlea Poland

1. Once Upon A Time there was a land called Unicornia.
2. The King of Unicornia was named Jerry the Unicorn King. He did not care for his fellow unicorns.
3. One day the unicorns decided to leave Unicornia and go to Unicornland.
4. So they left, and Jerry had no one to talk to.
5. For that reason Jerry decided to change his ways. He told his fellow unicorns what he had decided.
6. Then they all moved back to Unicornia.

Corrections and Comments

Student Name:	**Date:**
Example: Line 1 → Once upon a time there was a land called Unicornia. The King of Unicornia	
was named Jerry.	
Note: The phrase "the Unicorn King" is unnecessary; the first part of the sentence says that.	

Edited Version: Jerry The Unicorn King by McKinlea Poland

STORY	COMMENTS
~~Once Upon A Time~~ [***Once upon a time***] there was a land called Unicornia. The King of Unicornia was named Jerry. ~~the Unicorn King.~~ *[Editor's Note: The phrase "the Unicorn King" is unnecessary; the first part of the sentence says that.]*	**1. This story clearly states a situation.** "The King of Unicornia was named Jerry. He did not care for his fellow unicorns. One day the unicorns decided to leave Unicornia..." *CCSS ELA-Literacy.W.5.3.a*
He did not care ~~for~~ [***about***] ~~his fellow~~ [***the***] unicorns [***in his kingdom.***] *[Editor's Note: "He did not care about..." is a more precise phrase because it implies a lack of feeling or caring toward his subjects, whereas "He did not care for..." can imply a dislike for his subjects or his lack of desire to help them physically in some way.* *Also, he is a king and kings rule over citizens or subjects. "Fellow" implies the subjects are equals to the king, which they are not.]*	**2. It is obvious there is a narrator** (who happens to be the author) and she tells the story in the third person (a story written in the third person uses the pronouns "he," "she," "it"). *CCSS ELA-Literacy.W.5.3.a*
One day the unicorns decided to leave Unicornia and go to Unicornland. So they left, and Jerry had no one to [***rule over or***] talk to.	**3. The sequence of events unfolds naturally, in a time sequence and the essay uses the narrative technique of responses of characters to situations.** The author describes the setting and the main character (the kingdom of Unicornia and its ruler), then the problem ("He did not care about his fellow unicorns.") then an outcome (result) from the problem

STORY	COMMENTS
	("One day the unicorns decided to leave Unicornia…") then another outcome ("So Jerry decided to change his ways.") and a final outcome ("He contacted his former subjects about his decision to change his ways and convinced them to move back to Unicornia."). *CCSS ELA-Literacy.W.5.3.a and CCSS ELA-Literacy.W.5.3.b*
For that reason Jerry decided to change his ways.	**4. Transitional words** Time transition: "Once upon a time"; "One day the unicorns decided to leave…" Cause transition: "For that reason Jerry decided to change his ways."
~~He told his fellow unicorns what he had decided. Then they all moved back to Unicornia.~~ [*He contacted his former subjects about his decision to change his ways and convinced them to move*] back to Unicornia.	**5. Concrete words, sensory details.** "He did not care about the unicorns in his kingdom." "One day the unicorns decided to leave Unicornia…" "So they left, and Jerry had no one to rule over or talk to." "He contacted his former subjects about his decision to change his ways and convinced them to move back to Unicornia." *CCSS ELA-Literacy.W.5.3.d*
	6. Conclusion. " …and convinced them to move back to Unicornia." *CCSS ELA-Literacy.W.5.3.e*

STORY	COMMENTS
	7. Missing information. **7.1** “He did not care about the unicorns in his kingdom.” The author could have given some examples of how the King did not care about his unicorns. That would more completely explain why they left Unicornia. **7.2** “For that reason Jerry decided to change his ways.” If the author had given some examples of how the King did not care about the unicorns he ruled (as suggested in paragraph 7.1 above), then the author could have explained how Jerry was going to change his ways.

Your Suggested Topics:

Exercises Ideas:

1. Invasion of the space aliens
2. The day I met my favorite (movie star, singer, athlete etc.)
3. A mysterious (tweet, email, letter etc.)
4. An unusual (classmate, friend, relative etc.)
5. If I were president (of my class, of the United States)

Text Types and Purposes Category: Narrative Nonfiction

Standard: CCSS.ELA-Literacy.W.5.3

Narrative Nonfiction: A story or account of events or experiences that are true, that is, that actually occurred. Point of view: You normally write narrative nonfiction stories in the first person or third person.

Title: Making Ken-Ken Happy by McKinlea Poland

1. I love making Ken-Ken happy. She is my little sister.

2. There are lots of ways to make her happy. One way is playing her favorite games. Her favorite games are cops and robbers, hide and seek, freeze tag, and piggyback rides.

3. Another way I can make her happy is by giving her ice cream. She likes three scoops of strawberry and some rainbow sprinkles.

4. Another way I can make her happy is by helping her do homework. Ken-Ken has math, spelling and reading every night.

5. One other way I can make Ken-Ken happy is by being nice to her. I could not get mad when she messes with my stuff. I could also let her play with me even when I want to play by myself.

6. Ken-Ken is the best sister I could ever have. I love her even when I get mad and frustrated. I really like making her happy.

Corrections and Comments

Student Name:	**Date:**
Example: Line #1 → ~~I love making Ken-Ken happy. She is my little sister.~~	
I love making my little sister Ken-Ken happy.	

Edited Version: Making Ken-Ken Happy by McKinlea Poland

STORY	COMMENTS
~~I love making Ken-Ken happy. She is my little sister.~~ [***I love making my little sister Ken-Ken happy.***]	1. **This story clearly states a situation.** "I love making Ken-Ken happy. She is my little sister." *CCSS ELA-Literacy.W.5.3.a* 2. **It is obvious that there is a narrator** (who happens to be the author) and she tells the story in the first person (a story written in the first person uses the pronouns "my", "I", "we.") *CCSS ELA-Literacy.W.5.3.a* 3. **The sequence of events unfold naturally.** This story contains a listing of actions the author takes to make her sister happy. The actions are listed in random order, which is fine because the order in which the actions are done is not important. *CCSS ELA-Literacy.W.5.3.a*
There are lots of ways to make her happy. One way is playing her favorite games, [***which are:***] cops and robbers, hide and seek, freeze tag, and piggyback rides.	4. **Narrative techniques used. Descriptive details.** "Her favorite games are cops and robbers, hide and seek, freeze tag, and piggyback rides."; "She likes three scoops of strawberry and some rainbow sprinkles."; "Ken-Ken has math, spelling and reading every night."

STORY	COMMENTS
Another way ~~I can make her happy~~ is by giving her ice cream. She likes three scoops of strawberry and some rainbow sprinkles.	**5. Responses of characters to situations.** In the author's own words, the actions she takes to make Ken-Ken happy make her happy. *CCSS ELA-Literacy.W.5.3.b and* *CCSS ELA-Literacy.W.5.3.d*
Another way ~~I can make her happy~~ is by helping her do homework. Ken-Ken has math, spelling and reading every night.	
One other way ~~I can make Ken-Ken happy~~ is by being nice to her. I could not get mad when she messes with my stuff. I could also let her play with me even when I want to play by myself.	**6. Changing tense.** "I could not get mad…" implies that this has not happened yet. Same for "I could also let her play with me…." This is in contrast with the rest of the story that is written in the present tense, implying that the author has already done the other actions that make Ken-Ken happy. **7. Missing information.** As a reader, I am curious how Ken-Ken got her name. I wish the author had explained that. **8. Transitions.** **Addition transition:** "*Another* way is by giving her ice cream"; "Another way is by helping her do homework." **Time transition:** "I love her even *when*…" *CCSS ELA-Literacy.W.5.3.c*
Ken-Ken is the best sister I could ever have. I love her even when ~~I get~~ [***she makes me***] mad and frustrated. I really like making her happy.	**9. Conclusion.** "I really like making her happy." is a conclusion. *CCSS ELA-Literacy.W.5.3.e*

Title: Colorado by McKinlea Poland

1. Have you been to Colorado before?
   I went there because I go every two years. I went there with my dad's side of the family. I went to ride horses, ride the tram and feed the chipmunks.

2. I saw my grandma Gigi. I also saw my aunt who lives in Dallas, Aunt Fara. My family screamed at each other while in the bumper cars. We also bumped into each other. Have you been in bumper cars before? I saw my cousin Emma. I also saw my cousin Dailey. We had a race who would slide down the fastest. We also slid down different colors.

I have been waiting to ride the slide! We stuck our feet in the river. We also swam in the river and it was so cold we felt like ice cubes. We fed cute and fuzzy chipmunks. We ate lunch at my cousin Addley, Ashbee and Anslea's cabin. Have you been in a cabin before? I soaked my dad and sister. I also went through a plastic cave. I rode in the passenger seat. My uncles drove me crazy. I put lots of salt on my eggs. I also put loads of syrup on my pancakes. On the horse trail, we saw a baby bunny. We rode on the trail up and down the mountain.

3. I loved it and can't wait to go again. I also can't wait to see my family again.

Corrections and Comments

Student Name:	Date:
Example: Paragraph #1 → Have you [***ever***] been to Colorado ~~before~~?	

Edited Version: Colorado by McKinlea Poland

STORY	COMMENTS
Have you [***ever***] been to Colorado ~~before~~? ~~I went there because~~ I go [***there***] every two years~~. I went there~~ with my dad's side of the family, ~~I went~~ to ride horses, ride the tram and feed the chipmunks.	**1. This story clearly states a situation.** "Have you ever been to Colorado? I go there every two years with my dad's side of the family, to ride horses, ride the tram and feed the chipmunks." *CCSS ELA-Literacy.W.5.3.a*
I saw my grandma Gigi. I also saw my aunt who lives in Dallas, Aunt Fara. My family screamed at each other while in the bumper cars. We also bumped into each other. Have you [***ever***] been in bumper cars ~~before~~?	**2. It is obvious that there is a narrator** (who happens to be the author) and she tells the story in the first person (a story written in the first person uses the pronouns ""I", "my", "we.") *CCSS ELA-Literacy.W.5.3.a*
I saw my cousin Emma. I also saw my cousin Dailey. We had a race [***to find out***] who would slide down the fastest. We also slid down different colors. I have been waiting to ride the slide!	**3. The sequence of events unfold naturally, in a time sequence.** This story contains a listing of events the author experiences. The events are listed in random order, which is fine because the order in which the events take place is not important. *CCSS ELA-Literacy.W.5.3.a*
[Author should start a new paragraph] We stuck our feet in the river. We also swam in the river and it was so cold we felt like ice cubes. We fed cute and fuzzy chipmunks. We ate lunch at my cousin Addley, Ashbee and Anslea's cabin. Have you been in a cabin before? I soaked my dad and sister. I also ~~went~~ [***rode***] through a plastic cave. I rode in the passenger seat. My uncles drove me crazy. I put lots of salt on my eggs. I also put loads of syrup on my pancakes. On the horse trail, we saw a baby bunny. We rode on the trail up and down the mountain.	**4. Narrative techniques used.** **Description:** "We stuck our feet in the river. We also swam in the river and it was so cold we felt like ice cubes."; "We fed cute and fuzzy chipmunks."; "My family screamed at each other while in the bumper cars. We also bumped into each other."

STORY	COMMENTS
	5. Bonding the reader with the author: "Have you ever been to Colorado before?"; "Have you ever been in bumper cars before?"; "Have you been in a cabin before?" This is a good technique because it causes the reader to think about the answer to the author's question; it strengthens the bond between author and reader. *CCSS ELA-Literacy.W.5.3.b* **6. Responses of characters to situations.** "My family screamed at each other while in the bumper cars."; "...swam in the river and it was so cold we felt like ice cubes."; "My uncles drove me crazy." *CCSS ELA-Literacy.W.5.3.b* **7. Concrete words, sensory details.** "My family screamed..."; "it was so cold we felt like ice cubes."; "I loved it..." *CCSS ELA-Literacy.W.5.3.d*
I loved it and can't wait to go again. I also can't wait to see my family again.	**8. Conclusion.** "I loved it and can't wait to go again. I also can't wait to see my family again." *CCSS ELA-Literacy.W.5.3.e*
	9. Missing information. **9.1** "I saw my grandma Gigi. I also saw my aunt who lives in Dallas, Aunt Fara."; "I saw my cousin Emma. I also saw my cousin Dailey."

STORY	COMMENTS
	Suggestions: This story would be even more interesting if the author gave at least one fact or detail about each relative she met. For example, their appearance (cowgirl, hippie, elegant), their personalities (my cousin Dailey told me about the calf roping competitions he participates in; Aunt Fara told me about the beauty contest she won.) *From reading several of the activities, it sounds like the author spent some time at an amusement park. She should have mentioned that.* **9.2** "We ate lunch at my cousin Addley, Ashbee and Anslea's cabin." *The sentence "Have you been in a cabin before?" is a perfect lead-in to a description of the cabin. For example, it did not have indoor plumbing, so we had to pump the water each time we needed it, and the bathroom was an outhouse located outside with no flush toilet– yuck!* **9.3** "I also rode through a plastic cave. I rode in the passenger seat." *Where was the cave – an amusement park, the family's backyard? You mentioned "ride the tram" in the first paragraph – is this what you rode in through the cave? Describe the tram. And want did you see inside the cave?* **9.4** "I soaked my dad and sister…" *with what? A hose?* **9.5** "We had a race *to find out* who would slide down the fastest." *How tall was the slide? What did it look like? Who won the race?*

STORY	COMMENTS
	9.6 "We also slid down different colors." *What does this mean? Need an explanation.* **9.7** "My uncles drove me crazy." *Explain how?* **9.8** "On the horse trail…" *Describe the experience of meeting your horse, saddling the horse, riding the horse.*

Title: The Best Day Ever by Emily Adams

I was sitting in my room, dressed with my backpack sitting next to me. My mom yelled from the bottom of the staircase "Emily, it's time to go!" I grabbed my backpack and ran so fast down the stairs. We met my dad at the door and I ran and opened it, forgetting that the alarm was on. "Emily, really? Please turn the alarm off before you go outside," my dad complained, wanting to go. "Okay, okay. Now let's go!" I replied, anxious to go to school. My grandma showed up in the driveway as we walked out the door.

We ran to the car and all climbed in. I was so jumpy in my seat I was so excited that I nearly shook the car. We got to the school and climbed out of the car. I ran to the sidewalk and started to run across the street. My dad ran up and grabed my arm just in time.

We finally got across the street and walked into the building. There were so many parents! I walked into the gym. I was looking through the window and waved at my parents as they walked away. Right then, I knew the best day ever was about to begin.

Corrections and Comments

Student Name:	**Date:**
Example: In first sentence → I was sitting in my room, dressed with my backpack ~~sitting~~ [lying] next to me.	

Edited Version: The Best Day Ever by Emily Adams

STORY	COMMENTS
I was sitting in my room, dressed with my backpack ~~sitting~~ [lying] next to me. My mom yelled from the bottom of the staircase "Emily, it's time to go!" I grabbed my backpack and ran ~~so fast~~ down the stairs. We met my dad at the door and I ~~ran and~~ opened it, forgetting that the alarm was on. "Emily, really? Please turn the alarm off before you go outside," my dad complained, wanting to go. "Okay, okay. Now let's go!" I replied, anxious to go to school. My grandma showed up in the driveway as we walked out the door.	**1. This story clearly states a situation.** "I was so excited that I nearly shook the car. We got to the school and climbed out of the car." "Right then, I knew the best day ever was about to begin." *CCSS ELA-Literacy.W.5.3.a*
[Author should start a new paragraph.] We ran to the car and all climbed in. I was so ~~jumpy~~ [***restless***] in my seat [***and***] so excited that I ~~nearly~~ [***actually***] ~~shook~~ [***vibrated***] the car. We got to the school and climbed out of the car. I ran to the sidewalk and started to run across the street. My dad ran up and [***grabbed my arm just in time to avoid being hit by a car or school bus***].	**2. It is obvious that there is a narrator** (who happens to be the author) and she tells the story in the first person (a story written in the first person uses the pronouns "my," "I," "we.") *CCSS ELA-Literacy.W.5.3.a*
[Author should start a new paragraph.] We finally ~~got across~~ [***were able to cross***] the street and walk into the ~~building~~ [***school***]. There were so many parents! I walked into the gym. I was looking through the window and waved at my parents as they walked away. *[Editor's note: Suggest that this be added to the last paragraph:*	**3. The sequence of events unfold naturally, in a time sequence.** There is a logical time sequence as follows: waiting in her room, leaving in the car, arriving at the school, entering the school, and waving goodbye to her parents. *CCSS ELA-Literacy.W.5.3.a*

STORY	COMMENTS
I was so happy to be in middle school. I had grown bored in elementary school, and was finally leaving it behind, and starting middle school.]	**4. Narrative techniques used**
Middle school: More interesting classes, more extracurricular activities, and the chance to meet other students who had attended the other elementary school. I am so happy this day has arrived!] Right then, I knew the best day ever was about to begin.	**Creating reader interest**: The title builds reader interest because the reader wants to find out what happens to make this the "best day ever" for the author. Also, the author describes her emotions clearly; she is excited about something, but the author never tells the reader why. **Suggestion**: Readers might guess that for the author, this is the first day of a new school year, and she has graduated to a grade in a different building, both events causing excitement. But I think the author should explain the reasons for her excitement in the conclusion of the story, rewarding those readers who have figured it out and not leaving those who have not wondering. See the Editor's note for a suggested Addition to the ending. *CCSS ELA-Literacy.W.5.3.b* **5. Responses of characters to situations.** "I grabbed my backpack and ran…"; "… anxious to go to school."; "We ran to the car…I was so jumpy…"; "We got to the school ... I ran to the sidewalk and started to run across the street." *CCSS ELA-Literacy.W.5.3.b and* *CCSS ELA-Literacy.W.5.3.d*

STORY	COMMENTS
	6. Transitional words and phrases - links between ideas. "Right then…" *CCSS ELA-Literacy.W.5.3.c* **7. Conclusion.** "Right then, I knew the best day ever was about to begin." *CCSS ELA-Literacy.W.5.3.e*

Title: Learning Under the Dark Dome by Vibhu M. Krishnaswamy

1. My day started normally. I got up, brushed my teeth and got ready for school. Suddenly I remembered I was going on a field trip. I was very excited! I rushed to the bus stop, but I still missed the bus. I got on a different bus and made it to the school. I thought it wouldn't be such a good day after all. First I had my math class and then I went to eat breakfast. Later we got a chance to play outside for about an hour. I was exhausted after all that playing. The weather was not good at all. It looked like it was going to rain.

2. Suddenly, I heard my teacher say "Come and stand in the line children". We formed a line and got into the buses and the journey to the Planetarium began! While going we played many games like charades and word building. As soon as we stopped, everyone was so excited, they started screaming.

3. We got down the bus and the sports teacher yelled "Form a single line". We formed lines according to our classes and sections. First section A went then section B, which was my section. We walked for five minutes and on the way we got to see the science park. Then we reached a gate which lead to the planetarium. In the hallway walls had murals of many constellations with information about them. There was another poster which was about Mars, the King of War.
   We came to a pathway which lead to the inside of the planetarium. The security guard was not very polite. He was very harsh. We then entered a huge dark dome. I luckily got the front row seat. I sat with three of my friends. Everybody finally quieted down and the program started. The first video was about how to stop light pollution. It was an interesting movie. I learnt that we should not beam street lights into the night sky. Without light pollution people can enjoy a full night sky. We watched another video which was long, but fun. We learnt how the planets and constellations were formed. When the program was over, we walked out of the dark dome and into the glistening sun. My eyes hurt so much, that I could barely see.

4. While going back, the sports teacher made us form a line and we happily went back to the bus. After few minutes, we got yummy snacks. The teachers gave us chocolate milk and some cookies. On the way back, we played atlas, solved my Rubik's cube and played many games. I had a really good time. We stopped near the pre-nursery block and waited for our parents to pick us up. My dad was waiting for me there and I was telling my teacher that my dad hadn't come yet as the other students left earlier than me. My dad came out of the blue and said "need a ride?" I thanked my teacher and went home.

5. Today was an awesome day! I wish school would always be like this, going to fun places like a planetarium and learning so many things in a short period of time instead of my boring Geography class.

Corrections and Comments

Student Name:	**Date:**
Example: Paragraph #2 → We formed a line and got into the buses and the journey to the ~~P~~ [***p***]lanetarium began!	

Edited Version: Learning Under the Dark Dome by Vibhu M. Krishnaswamy

STORY	COMMENTS
My day started normally. I got up, brushed my teeth and got ready for school. Suddenly I remembered I was going on a field trip. I was very excited! I rushed to the bus stop, but I still missed the bus. I got on a different bus and made it to the school. I thought it wouldn't be such a good day after all. First I had my math class and then I went to eat breakfast. Later we got a chance to play outside for about an hour. I was exhausted after all that playing. The weather was not good at all. It looked like it was going to rain.	1. **This story clearly states a situation.** "Suddenly I remembered I was going on a field trip." and "The journey to the Planetarium began!" *CCSS ELA-Literacy.W.5.3.a* 2. **It is obvious that there is a narrator** (who happens to be the author) and he tells the story in the first person (a story written in the first person uses the pronouns "my," "I," "we.") *CCSS ELA-Literacy.W.5.3.a*
Suddenly, I heard my teacher say "Come and stand in the line children". We formed a line and got into the buses and the journey to the ~~P~~ [***p***]lanetarium began! While going we played many games like charades and word building. As soon as we stopped, everyone was so excited, they started screaming.	3. **The sequence of events unfold naturally, in a time sequence.** "My day started normally" (got up, brushed teeth); "I rushed to the bus stop;"…made it to school"; "…math class"; "…got into the buses…journey to the Planetarium…"; "…entered a huge dark dome"; …went back to the bus." *CCSS ELA-Literacy.W.5.3.a*
We got ~~down~~ [***off***] the bus and the sports teacher yelled "Form a single line". We formed lines according to our classes and sections. ~~First section A went then section B, which was my section.~~ *[Editor's note: Delete this; it is not necessary and adds nothing to the story.]*	
We walked for five minutes and on the way we got to see the science park. Then we reached a gate which led to the planetarium. In the hallway walls had murals of many constellations with information about them. There was another poster which was about Mars, the King of War.	

STORY

[author should start a new paragraph]

We came to a pathway which led to the inside of the planetarium. ~~The security guard was not very polite. He was very harsh.~~ *[Editor's note: Delete this; it is not necessary and adds nothing to the story.]*

We then entered a huge dark dome. I luckily got the front row seat. I sat with three of my friends. Everybody finally quieted down and the program started. The first video was about how to stop light pollution. It was an interesting movie. I learnt that we should not beam street lights into the night sky. Without light pollution people can enjoy a full night sky. We watched another video which was long, but fun. We learnt how the planets and constellations were formed. When the program was over, we walked out of the dark dome and into the glistening sun. My eyes hurt so much, that I could barely see.

While going back, the sports teacher made us form a line and we happily went back to the bus. After few minutes, we got yummy snacks. The teachers gave us chocolate milk and some cookies. On the way back, we played atlas, solved my Rubik's cube and played many games. I had a really good time. We stopped near the pre-nursery block and waited for our parents to pick us up. My dad was waiting for me there and I was telling my teacher that my dad hadn't come yet as the other students left earlier than me. My dad came out of the blue and said "need a ride?" I thanked my teacher and went home.

COMMENTS

4. Narrative techniques used.

Description:

"…we played many games like charades and word building";

"In the hallway walls had murals of many constellations with information about them. There was another poster which was about Mars, the King of War."; "We then entered a huge dark dome."; "… out of the dark dome and into the glistening sun."

The descriptions of the videos were well done – they identified the main topic in each video.

CCSS ELA-Literacy.W.5.3.b

5. Responses of characters to situations.

"Suddenly I remembered I was going on a field trip. I was very excited! I rushed…"; "I was exhausted after all that playing."; "…we stopped, everyone was so excited, they started screaming."; "The security guard was not very polite. He was very harsh";

"It was an interesting movie."; "My eyes hurt so much…."

CCSS ELA-Literacy.W.5.3.b

6. Transitional words and phrases - links between ideas.

Time transition: suddenly, later, then, when.

Addition transition: and, first.

Contrast transition: but, yet

CCSS ELA-Literacy.W.5.3.c

STORY	COMMENTS
Today was an [***awesome***] day! I wish school would always be like this, going to fun places like a planetarium and learning so many things in a short period of time instead of my boring ~~G~~ [***g***]eography class.	**7. Concrete words, sensory details.** "...games like charades and word building.";"... murals of many constellations...";"...they started screaming."; "I had a really good time." *CCSS ELA-Literacy.W.5.3.d* **8. Conclusion.** "Today was an awesome day! I wish school would always be like this, going to fun places like a planetarium and learning so many things in a short period of time instead of my boring geography class." *CCSS ELA-Literacy.W.5.3.e* **9. Less familiar usage of word.** "learnt" is correctly used, but "learned" is used more frequently by most authors. **10. Missing information.** **10.1** The author says: "Suddenly I remembered I was going on a field trip. I was very excited!" Suggestion: Why not mention here that the trip is to a planetarium? Surely the teacher announced where they were going when the teacher announced the trip. **10.2** "...on the way we got to see the science park." Suggestion: If you are going to mention the science park, why not tell the reader something about it? Otherwise, don't mention it.

STORY	COMMENTS
	11. Relationship of Title to Content. The title implies that the main topic is what the author learned under the dark dome (the planetarium). Although the story describes the interior of the planetarium and the two videos, it also describes events that take place before and after the students enter and leave the planetarium. Therefore, a better title might be something like "My Exciting Day at School."

Your Suggested Topics:

Exercises Ideas:

1. My (wonderful, terrible) vacation
2. My school trip
3. My first (play, concert, game)
4. My best friend
5. Meeting a famous person

Text Types and Purposes Category: Opinion

Standard: CCSS.ELA-Literacy.W.5.1

Opinion: A belief or judgment about which the believer is not absolutely certain or positive.

- Can be written from first person or third person point of view
- Clearly state your opinion and reasons for that opinion
- Can include the opinions of others besides the author

Title: Tacos: A Great Food For Everyone
by Jasmine Brunton

1. Tacos are a great food that can be eaten in many different ways. I absolutely love tacos because they can be eaten in so many different ways. Tacos are one my favorite foods because you can make them in many different ways. People like them with different ingredients in them but I like them my certain way.

2. I love to eat Taco's with lettuces, cheese, and medium salsa sauce on a soft shell. The soft shells are so delicious. I can eat 2 or 3 of them in one meal. I love to eat them for Lunch, or for Dinner. With Tacos you can eat them just about any time of the day, and even for a snack.

3. I have even eaten them for Breakfast! You can put just about anything in a soft taco shell. I like to put scrambled eggs, ham, bacon, and cheese into my soft taco shell, and have them for breakfast. If you have never tried this you really need to soon!

4. I even love to eat them on a hard taco shell. I like to put my favorite toppings on these hard shells. My favorite part of the hard shell tacos is how they crunch when you bite into them. You should be warned sometimes the shell will break apart, and make quite the mess. Make sure you have a napkin because; eating them like this can really be messy.

5. I absolutely love tacos, and I think you will too if you don't already. Once you try one of the different ways I love to eat Tacos, I think you will agree. I know some people might not like Tacos but in the end they will always be my favorite food to eat!

Corrections and Comments

Student Name:	**Date:**
Example: In first line → Tacos are a great food. ~~that can be eaten in many different ways.~~	

Edited Version: Tacos: A Great Food For Everyone
by Jasmine Brunton

ESSAY

Tacos are a great food. ~~that can be eaten in many different ways.~~ I absolutely love tacos because they can be eaten in so many different ways. Tacos are one my favorite foods because you can make them in many different ways. People like them with different ingredients ~~in them~~ but I like them my ~~certain~~ way.

~~I love to eat~~ [***My way is***] ~~T~~ [*t*]aco's with lettuce ~~s~~, cheese and medium salsa sauce on a soft shell. The soft shells are so delicious. I can eat 2 or 3 of them in one meal. I love to eat them [***made my way***] for ~~L~~ [*l*]unch or for ~~D~~ [*d*]inner. With ~~T~~ [*t*]aco's you can eat them just about any time of the day, ~~and~~ even for a snack.

I have even eaten them for ~~B~~ [*b*]reakfast! You can put just about anything in a soft taco shell. [***My way for making a taco for breakfast is***] ~~I like~~ to put scrambled eggs, ham, bacon and cheese into ~~my~~ [***a***] soft taco shell. ~~and have them for breakfast.~~ If you have never tried this you really need too soon!

I even love to eat them on a hard taco shell. I like to put my favorite toppings on these hard shells. My favorite part of the hard shell tacos is how they

COMMENTS

1. This essay introduces a topic clearly.

"Tacos are a great food. I absolutely love tacos because they can be eaten in so many different ways."

"…because you can make them in many different ways."

CCSS.ELA.W5.1.a

2. This essay states an opinion.

"I absolutely love tacos because they can be eaten in so many different ways."; If you have never tried this you really need to soon!"; "With taco's you can eat them just about any time of the day, and even for a snack."; "I absolutely love tacos, and I think you will too if you don't already. Once you try one of the different ways I love to eat tacos, I think you will agree."

CCSS.ELA.W5.1.a

ESSAY	COMMENTS
crunch when you bite into them. You should be warned sometimes the shell will break apart, and make quite the mess. Make sure you have a napkin because eating them like this can really be messy.	**3. Ideas are logically grouped to support the author’s purpose, including logically ordered reasons that support the author’s opinion.** **3.1** The introductory paragraph states the topic and the author’s opinion. **3.2** The remaining paragraphs provide details that support the author’s opinions about why tacos are a great food and why she loves them. **4. Link opinions and reasons using different kinds of transitions.** *Cause transition:* “I absolutely love tacos *because* they can be eaten…”; “…*because* you can make them…” *Contrast transition:* “I know some people might not like taco’s *but* in the end…” *CCSS.ELA.W5.1.c*
I absolutely love tacos, and I think you will too if you don’t already. Once you try one of the different ways I love to eat ~~T~~ [*t*]aco’s, I think you will agree. I know some people might not like tacos but in the end they will always be my favorite food to eat!	**5. The last paragraph is a concluding statement.** “I absolutely love tacos, and I think you will too if you don’t already. Once you try one of the different ways I love to eat tacos. I think you will agree. I know some people might not like tacos but in the end they will always be my favorite food to eat!” *CCSS.ELA.W5.1.d*

Title: School Uniforms: Good or Bad? by Emily Adams

1. I think school uniforms would be good for all schools, but for now, let's just stick to our school, Sunny Valley Elementary School, "home of the best kids." That's what we all say, but what goes on inside is another story.

2. In this article you will read about, and possibly learn, what uniforms can change in this school, like the fact that judging people by their clothes would stop, how you can personalize them, and how much more impressive our school would be with them. Also, you will learn how you can personalize them."
   To begin with, judging people by their clothes? That would stop for sure when we add uniforms to this school. Let's say someone had an odd, interesting outfit. What would we do? We would JUDGE him/her. That's not what you want Sunny Valley kids doing, do you? Well, uniforms would stop that. Why? Because when we are all wearing the same thing, you can't judge anyone. Basically, uniforms mean no more judging.
   Another reason why is that we won't look exactly alike, because you can personalize them to give them your own little touches.
   Adding on to what I said before, we would look the same, but not completely. Maybe you like glitter but have to wear a uniform. Well, just add a sparkly bow or a cute belt, and you would have an adorable personalized outfit. Just go with the flow and express your little touch.

3. Pursuing this further, we all know the principals are always trying to give us little impressive touchups. Tucking in our t-shirts. Great idea, but I know we can all do better. Just get rid of the tuck and bring in a highly sophisticated, amazingly impressive uniform which will make sure we receive amazing comments and leave everyone with a stunned look on their face, expesially Sunny Valley school board members and staff.

   To sum it all up, uniforms are the best choice for the school. If uniforms are required, many more improvements will come, like no more being judged by what you wear, that they are supremely easy to personalize, and they will give that very impressive touch we've all been looking for. I have one more question for you: Are you ready to jump on the train for successful uniforms? Now it's all up to you.

Corrections and Comments

Student Name:	**Date:**
Example: Paragraph #2 → In this article you will read ~~about, and possibly learn, what uniforms can change in this school,~~ ***how uniforms can change this school***.	

Edited Version: School Uniforms: Good or Bad? by Emily Adams

ESSAY	COMMENTS
I think school uniforms would be good for all schools, but for now, let's just stick to our school, Sunny Valley Elementary School, "home of the best kids." That's what we all say, but what goes on inside is another story.	**1. This essay introduces a topic clearly.** "I think school uniforms would be good for all schools…"; "In this article you will read how uniforms can change this school." **2. This essay states an opinion.** "I think school uniforms would be good for all schools…"; "Let's begin with judging people by their clothes? That would stop for sure when we add uniforms to this school."; "Basically, uniforms mean no more judging people based on what they wear." ; "To sum it all up, uniforms are the best thing for the school." *CCSS.ELA.W5.1.a*
In this article you will read ~~about, and possibly learn, what uniforms can change in this school,~~ [***how uniforms can change this school***]. ~~like the fact that~~ [***For example,***] judging people by their clothes would stop, ~~how you can personalize them~~, and ~~how much more impressive~~ our school would be [***much more impressive with***] them. Also, you will learn how you can personalize them." ~~To~~ [***Let's***] begin with judging people by their clothes? That would stop for sure when we add uniforms to this school. Let's say someone had an odd, interesting outfit. What would we do? We would JUDGE him/her. That's not what you want Sunny Valley kids	**3. Ideas are logically grouped to support the author's purpose, including logically ordered reasons that support the author's opinion.** **3.1** The introductory paragraph states the issue and the author's opinion. **3.2** The second paragraph summarizes the results if the author's opinion is supported and a policy requiring uniforms is accepted. **3.3** The third paragraph gives more details about a problem ("…judging people by their clothes?"), an opinion about the problem ("That's not what you want…"), and how the author's suggestion would

ESSAY	COMMENTS
doing, do you? Well, uniforms would stop that. Why? Because when we are all wearing the same thing, you can't judge anyone. Basically, uniforms mean no more judging [***people based on what they wear.***]	solve that problem ("…uniforms would stop that."; "…uniforms mean no more judging…."
~~Another reason why is that~~ [***Even though our appearances will be similar wearing uniforms, nonetheless***] we won't look exactly alike, because ~~you~~ [***we***] can personalize them ~~or~~ [***to***] give them ~~your~~ [***our***] own little touch*es*. Adding on to what I said before, we would look the same, but not completely. Maybe you like glitter but have to wear a uniform. Well, just add a sparkly bow or a cute belt, and you would have an adorable personalized outfit. Just go with the flow and express your little touch.	**3.4** The fourth paragraph defends the author's suggestion against students who might oppose it because they think uniforms make them all look alike, and unable to show any originality in their clothing, although the author does not directly state this as a problem. "Even though our appearances will be similar wearing uniforms, nonetheless we won't look exactly alike, because we can personalize them ~~or~~ to give them ~~your~~ our own little touch*es*."
Pursuing this further, we all know the principals are always trying to give us little impressive touchups. [***Telling us to tuck in***] ~~Tucking in~~ our T-shirts. Great idea, but I know we can all do better. Just get rid of the tuck and bring in a highly sophisticated, amazingly impressive uniform which will make sure we receive amazing comments and leave everyone with a stunned look ~~on their face,~~ ~~expesially~~ [***especially***] Sunny Valley school board members and staff. *[Editor's note: "everyone" is singular, "their" is plural, "face" is singular. Also, a stunned look can only happen on someone's face, so the phrase is unnecessary.]*	**3.5** The fifth paragraph points out how school principals are trying to make their students' appearances neater: "…we all know the principals are always trying to give us that little impressive touchups. Telling us to tuck in our T-shirts. Great idea, but I know we can all do better." And why the author's suggestion is a better way to achieve greater neatness: "…bring in a highly sophisticated, amazingly impressive uniform which will make sure we receive amazing comments…."

ESSAY	COMMENTS
To sum it all up, uniforms are the best choice for the school. If uniforms are required, many more improvements will come, like no more being judged by what you wear, that they are supremely easy to personalize, and they will give that very impressive touch we've all been looking for. I have one more question for you: Are you ready to jump on the train for successful uniforms? Now it's all up to you.	**3.6** The last paragraph is a concluding statement. *CCSS.ELA.W5.1.a and CSS.ELA.W5.1.b* **4. Link opinions and reasons using different kinds of transitions.** *Time transition:* "But *for now...*"; "*Let's begin* with..." *Contrast transition:* "*But* for now..." *Addition transition:* "*Adding on...*"; "Pursuing this *further...*" *Summary Transition:* "To sum it all up..." *CCSS.ELA.W5.1.c* **5. Provide a concluding statement related to the opinion presented.** The last paragraph is a summary of the opinions that the author has presented, with a challenge to the reader to support the author's opinion. *CCSS.ELA.W5.1.d* **6. Other Comments.** *Foreshadowing example:* "... but what goes on inside is another story." This statement creates interest by motivating the reader to continue reading to find out what goes on inside.

Title: Working For The Judicial Branch by Emily Adams

Dear President Obama:

1. My language arts teacher required that we write an essay on a government agency. I chose the Judicial Branch of the United States government. After researching it, I became very impressed with its functions and would like to work for it someday. For that reason, I have made a list of the reasons why, in my opinion, I would be a good worker in this branch. Do you think I have the right skills and attitude? Please reply.

2. This branch makes decisions that affect people's lives. I think I would do well with this because I love, love, love giving people orders and being in charge of making important decisions. I want to be able to help people end big arguments and disagreements. I want to help keep Americans safe by putting burglars, robbers and murderers in jail to keep them from harming people. I think it would be fun to be able to bang on my desk with a mallet and yell "UNCONSTITUTIONAL!" in my loud voice about something someone was trying to do.

3. In conclusion, now that you know something about me, what is your opinion about my ability to work in the Judicial Branch?

Sincerely,
Emily

Corrections and Comments

Student Name:	**Date:**
Example: **Essay introduces a topic clearly** → I chose the Judicial Branch of the United States government.	

Edited Version: Working For The Judicial Branch by Emily Adams

ESSAY	COMMENTS
Dear President Obama:	
My language arts teacher required that we write an essay on a government agency. I chose the Judicial Branch of the United States government. After researching it, I became very impressed with its functions and would like to work for it someday. For that reason, I have made a list of the reasons why I would be a good worker in this branch. Do you think I have the right skills and attitude? Please reply.	**1. This essay introduces a topic clearly.** "I chose the Judicial Branch of the United States government. After researching it, I became very impressed with its functions and would like to work for it someday. In this letter I have made a list of the reasons why I would be a good worker in this branch." *CCSS.ELA.W5.1.a* **2.** This essay asks the reader (President Obama) to state an opinion, but also **states the author's opinion that she thinks she is qualified to work for the Judicial Branch.** "For that reason, I have made a list of the reasons why I would be a good worker in this branch. Do you think I have the right skills and attitude? Please reply." *CCSS.ELA.W5.1.a* **3. The essay logically groups its content and provides reasons and details for supporting an opinion.** The first paragraph gives the background that leads to the author's purpose in writing, then states the author's purpose (to see if the President thinks she is qualified for the job), then gives reasons why she thinks she is qualified, then asks for the President's opinion. *CCSS.ELA.W5.1.a and CCSS.ELA.W5.1.b*

ESSAY	COMMENTS
This branch makes decisions that affect people's lives. I think I would do well with this because I love, love, love giving people orders and being in charge of making important decisions. I want to be able to help people end big arguments and disagreements. I want to help keep Americans safe by putting ~~burglars, robbers and murderers~~ [***criminals***] in jail to keep them from harming people. I think it would be fun to be able to bang on my desk with a ~~mallet~~ [***gavel***] and yell "UNCONSTITUTIONAL!" in my loud voice about something someone was trying to do. *[Editor's note: Gavel is a more logical choice than mallet because you are talking about a tool used in meetings, not a tool used in carpentry or metals work.]*	**4. The essay links opinions and reasons.** *Time transition:* "After researching it…"; "… would like to work for it someday." *Cause transition:* "For that reason…"; "...because I love, love, love giving people orders and being in charge of making important decisions." *Conclusion transition:* "In conclusion, now that you know something about me…"
In conclusion, now that you know something about me, what is your opinion about my ability to work in the Judicial Branch? Sincerely, Emily	**5. The last paragraph provides a concluding statement.** "In conclusion, now that you know something about me…" *CCSS.ELA.W5.1.d* **6. Other Comments.** *The author makes it clear that she would like a response from the President by asking questions:* "Do you think I have the right skills and attitude? Please reply." and "… what is your opinion about my ability to work in the Judicial Branch?"

Your Suggested Topics:

Exercises Ideas:

1. My favorite (movie, song, place to visit, hobby)
2. The most tasty, healthy snack foods
3. The best place to buy (clothes, pizza, ice cream etc.)
4. What I expect from a best friend
5. The most talented singer

Text Types and Purposes Category: Argument

Standard: CCSS.ELA-Literacy.W.5.1

Argument: A discussion in which differences in opinions (different points of view) are presented.

- Can present arguments in favor of an issue, opposed to an issue, or both (include opposite points of view on an issue).
- Must follow this format to meet Common Core standards:
    - clearly explain the issue
    - clearly explain your position on the issue
    - provide facts or opinions to support your position. Can include comment on an opposing position as well.
    - provide a concluding statement, which can be a summary of the position you have taken and/or recommendations for action your audience can take.
- Can be written in the first, second or third person.

Title: The Pros and Cons of Zoos by Emily Adams

1. One of my favorite memories from when I was little was going to a zoo. I loved looking at all the different animals and learning about them. But as I got older, I learned more and more about what happens there.

2. Zoos are found in almost every country in the world, but are they really all that good for the animals? In this essay you will learn the pros and cons of zoos. I hope by the end of this essay you have chosen either pro or con.

3. On the pro side of zoos, the animals on the outside of the zoos are being hunted for many different things like ivory, fur, and meat. When the animals are inside the zoos they are out of the danger of the hunters.

4. Another pro is that in the past the animals were being treated badly, but zoos have slowly stopped the harassment to where the animals are being treated like kings.

5. The third and final pro is that zoos are very informative about their different animals to people of all ages, many schools go on field trips to zoos so they can teach their students about the different animals.

6. On the con side, of zoos, as the zoos have many different animals, and in order to get the animals people from zoos have to go around the world and capture the animals which in a way, is animal cruelty.

7. The second reason against zoos is that when the animals are in confined spaces they develop negative psychological disorders and behaviors. For instance, have you ever seen the Tigers at the zoo pace around their exhibit? That isn't a natural behavior for a tiger, it is caused by stress related psychological behaviors.

8. The third and final con is when the animals are born in a zoo they know nothing about their natural habitat or sometimes their own kind. This isolation can be both sad and dangerous for the animals. If they were ever released, they might not be able to survive on their own.

9. The topic of zoos is very controversial to discuss. Zoos could be good or they could be bad. The decision is yours to make. Will you go for zoos and help keep them alive or will you work to abolish them? The decision is yours to make.

Corrections and Comments

Student Name:	**Date:**
Example: Essay introduces the topic clearly → One of my favorite memories from when I was little was going to a zoo.	

Edited Version: The Pros and Cons of Zoos by Emily Adams

ESSAY	COMMENTS
One of my favorite memories from when I was little was going to a zoo. I loved looking at all the different animals and learning about them. But as I got older, I learned more and more about ~~what happens there.~~ [***them and began to wonder if zoos***] ~~Zoos are found in almost every country in the world, but~~ are ~~they~~ really all that good for the animals? In this essay you will learn the pros and cons ~~of zoos.~~ [***that a zoo offers for animals, and***] I hope by the end of this essay you ~~have chosen either pro or con.~~ [***will have enough information to decide in favor or against having zoos.***]	**1. This essay introduces the topic clearly.** "One of my favorite memories from when I was little was going to a zoo." "But as I got older, I learned more and more about what happens there." "In this essay you will learn the pros and cons of zoos. I hope by the end of this essay you have chosen either pro or con." *CCSS.ELA-Literacy.W.5.1.a`*
On the pro side of zoos, the animals ~~on the~~ outside of the zoos are being hunted for ~~many different things like~~ [***their***] ivory, fur, and meat. ~~When the~~ Animals ~~are~~ inside the zoos ~~they~~ are ~~out of the danger of~~ [***protected from***] the hunters.	**2. The arguments on both sides are logically grouped and clearly stated.** "On the pro side of zoos…" "Another pro is that…" "The third and final pro is that…" "On the con side of zoos…" "The second reason against zoos…" "The third and final con is when…" *CCSS.ELA-Literacy.W.5.1.a*
[***What used to be a con in the past was that***] ~~Another pro is that in the past~~ the animals were being treated badly, but [***this is now a pro because the***] zoos have slowly stopped the harassment ~~where~~ [***and now treat***] the animals ~~are being treated~~ like kings. The third ~~and final~~ pro is that zoos ~~are very informative~~ [***give lots of information***] about their different animals to people of all ages, [***and***] many schools go on field trips to zoos so they can teach their students about the different animals.	

ESSAY	COMMENTS
On the con side, ~~of zoos, as the~~ zoos have many different animals, and in order to get ~~the animals~~ [***them they send***] people ~~from zoos have to go~~ around the world ~~and~~ [***to***] capture the animals which ~~in a way,~~ [***can result in***] ~~is~~ animal cruelty. The second reason against zoos is that when the animals are in confined spaces they develop negative psychological disorders and behaviors. For instance, have you ever seen the ~~T~~ [***t***]igers at the zoo pace around their exhibit? That isn't a natural behavior for a tiger; it is [***psychological behavior***] caused by stress~~-related~~ ~~psychological behaviors~~. The third and final con is when the animals are born in a zoo they know nothing about their natural habitat or sometimes their own kind. This isolation can be both sad and dangerous for the animals. If they were ever released, they might not be able to survive on their own.	**3. Logically ordered reasons supported by facts and details.** **3.1** See #2 for examples of logically ordered details (pros and cons). **3.2** Facts and details: "Zoos are found in almost every country in the world…" "…animals on the outside of the zoos are being hunted… ivory, fur, and meat." "…inside the zoos they are out of the danger of the hunters." "…animals were being treated badly but zoos have slowly stopped the harassment …" *Comment:* It would be a good idea for the author to show some proof that this has happened." "…the people from zoos have to go around the world and capture the animals which, in a way, is animal cruelty." "when the animals are in confined spaces they develop negative psychological disorders and behaviors…. the Tigers at the zoo pace around their exhibit?" *CCSS.ELA-Literacy.W.5.1.b*

ESSAY	COMMENTS
	4. Words, phrases and clauses that link arguments with supporting reasons and/or provide transitions. *Time transition:* "... from when I was little…" *Addition transition:* "Another…"; "second…"; "third…" *Contrast transition:* "But as I got older…"; "but zoos have slowly stopped…" *Illustration transition:* "For instance, have you ever seen the Tigers…" *CCSS.ELA-Literacy.W.5.1.c*
The topic of zoos is very controversial to discuss [***because there are pros and cons***]. ~~Zoos could be good or they could be bad.~~ ~~The decision is yours to make.~~ Will you ~~go for zoos~~ [***decide in favor of zoos***] and help keep them ~~alive~~ [***in existence***] or will you work to abolish them? The decision is yours to make.	**5. Concluding statement.** "The topic of zoos is very controversial to discuss. Zoos could be good or they could be bad. The decision is yours to make. Will you go for zoos and help keep them alive or will you work to abolish them? *CCSS.ELA-Literacy.W.5.1.d* **6. Bonding author and reader.** **6.1** "Zoos are found in almost every country in the world, but are they really all that good for the animals? In this essay you will learn the pros and cons of zoos. I hope by the end of this essay you have chosen either pro or con."

ESSAY	COMMENTS
	7. "The topic of zoos is very controversial to discuss. Zoos could be good or they could be bad. The decision is yours to make. Will you go for zoos and help keep them alive or will you work to abolish them?"

Title: Sporting Associations and Media Rights
By Vibhu Krishnaswamy

1. Sporting associations should be banned from selling media rights. A number of scams related to sporting associations such as FIFA, NFL, and IOC have come to light in the recent past. Sporting Associations are acquiring huge sums of money by selling Media Rights and other means. I would like to protest to this corrupt system so that games could be fair and fun!

2. As these associations are sporting associations, they should stay focused on running the sporting events efficiently and fairly. 50 years ago, there was only one video broadcast system which was Television. During the broadcast, only one big and famous TV channel would record the match live and sporting fans would watch it.

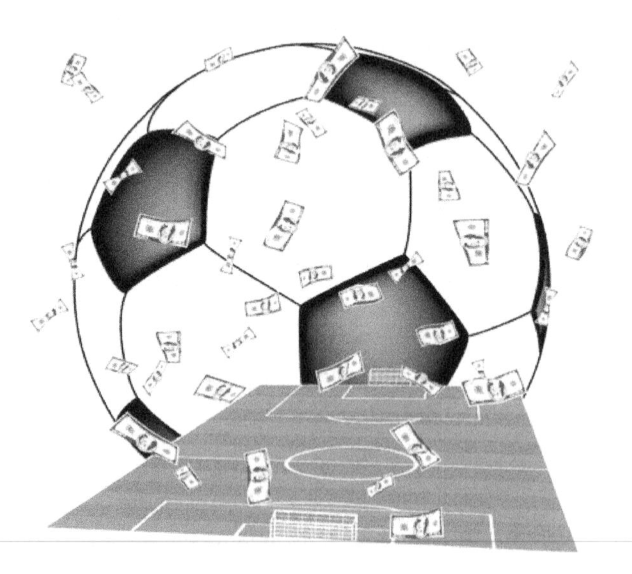

3. Nowadays, anyone can watch the match on their smartphone. Spectators can easily transmit sporting events using their mobile phones and internet. TV broadcasting companies could record high quality video and transmit it to their audience. By eliminating the financial element the officials are less likely to get involved in scams.

4. Sport enthusiasts would have access to free and personalized coverage and still have the option to watch professional coverage.

5. One of the Association's supporters might say that they need resources to run the organization and that takes money! If the company needs resources, they need to focus on getting those resources through other channels such as membership fees. They should be able to efficiently run sporting events with fraction of the money instead of hundreds of millions of dollars.

6. Therefore, I believe that sports would be fun and fair if financial incentive for corruption is removed. I would like banning sporting associations from entering into large deals with broadcast companies.

Corrections and Comments

Student Name:	Date:
Example: Line #1 → A number of scams related to sporting associations such as FIFA, NFL ***and*** IOC have come to light in the recent past.	

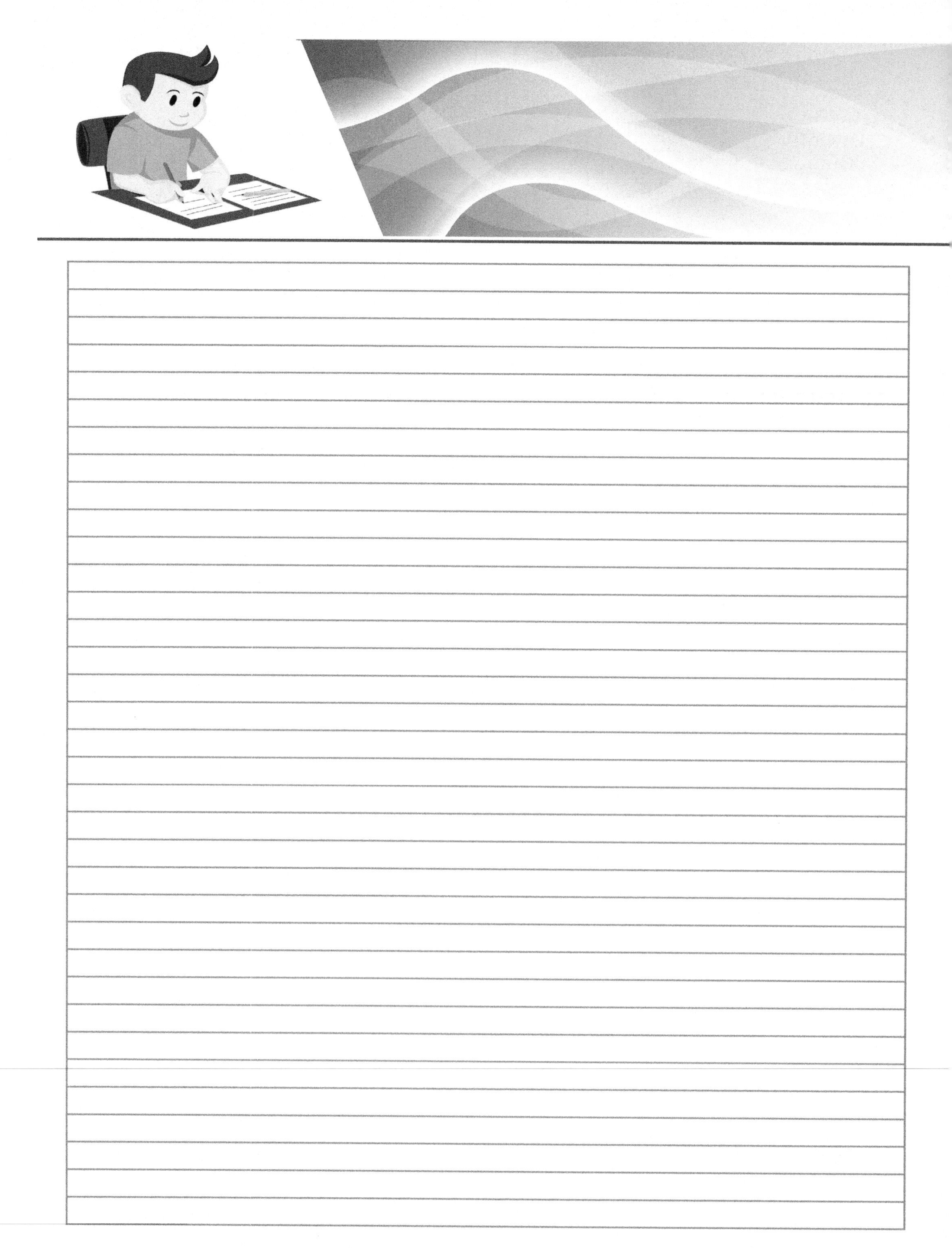

Edited Version: Sporting Associations and Media Rights
By Vibhu Krishnaswamy

ESSAY	COMMENTS
Sporting associations should be banned from selling media rights. A number of scams related to sporting associations such as FIFA, NFL [***and***] IOC have come to light in the recent past. Sporting ~~A~~ [***a***]ssociations are acquiring huge sums of money by selling ~~M~~ [***m***] edia ~~R~~ [***r***]ights and [***by***] other means [***and using some of the money for corrupt practices***]. I would like to protest ~~to~~ this corrupt system so that games could be fair and fun!	**1. This essay introduces the topic clearly.** "Sporting associations should be banned from selling media rights." "I would like to protest this corrupt system so that games could be fair and fun!" *CCSS.ELA-Literacy.W.5.1.a*
As these ~~associations~~ are sporting associations, they should stay focused on running the sporting events efficiently and fairly [***instead of acquiring huge sums of money by selling media rights.***] ~~50~~ [***Fifty***] years ago, there was only one video broadcast system, which was ~~T~~ [***t***]elevision. ~~During the broadcast, only one big and famous~~ [***Only one***] TV channel ~~would~~ [***was allowed to***] record the match live ~~and~~ [***to***] sporting fan[***s***]. ~~would watch it.~~ Nowadays, anyone can watch ~~the match~~ [***sporting events***] on their smartphones. Spectators can easily transmit sporting events using their mobile phones and the internet. [***If sporting associations stopped charging for media rights, then***] TV broadcasting companies could record high quality live video for free and transmit it to their audiences, [***covering their costs and earning profits by charging their advertisers for their ads.***]	**2. The arguments are logically grouped and clearly stated.** "A number of scams related to sporting associations such as FIFA, NFL, and IOC have come to light in the recent past. Sporting associations are acquiring huge sums of money by selling media rights and by other means…." "As these ~~associations~~ are sporting associations, they should stay focused on running the sporting events efficiently and fairly instead of acquiring huge sums of money by selling media rights." "Nowadays, anyone can watch sporting events on their smartphones. Spectators can easily transmit sporting events using their mobile phones and the internet." *CCSS.ELA-Literacy.W.5.1.a and* *CCSS.ELA-Literacy.W.5.1.b*

ESSAY	COMMENTS
By eliminating the charges for media rights, ~~financial element~~ the officials of the sponsoring associations are less likely to get involved in scams. Sports enthusiasts would have access to free and personalized coverage and still have the option to watch professional coverage.	**3. Words, phrases and clauses that link arguments with supporting reasons and/or provide transitions.** *Time transition: "Nowadays*, anyone can watch…" *Contrast transition:* "…running the sporting events efficiently and fairly *instead of* acquiring huge sums of money….”; “*instead of* acquiring huge sums of money by selling media rights.”
[***An opponent of this proposal***] ~~One of the Association's supporters~~ might say that they need monetary resources to run their ~~organization~~ [***association***] ~~and that takes money~~! If the ~~company~~ [***association***] needs resources, they need to focus on getting those resources through other channels, such as membership fees. They should be able to efficiently run sporting events with a fraction of the money instead of hundreds of millions of dollars.	*Effect transition:* “...protest this corrupt system *so that* games could be fair and fun!” *Summary transition:* “” *CCSS.ELA-Literacy.W.5.1.c*
Therefore, I believe that sports would be fun and fair if the financial incentive for corruption is removed. I would like [***to ban***] ~~banning~~ sporting associations from entering into large deals with broadcast companies.	**4. Concluding statement:** “Therefore, I believe that sports would be fun and fair if the financial incentive for corruption is removed. I would like to ban sporting associations from entering into large deals with broadcast companies.” *CCSS.ELA-Literacy.W.5.1.d*

Title: Smartphones and Tablets in the Classroom
by George Smith and Vibhu Krishnaswamy

1. Mrs. MacGregor, fifth grade English teacher, announced plans for a debate within her class. The topic will be: Should students be allowed to bring their smartphones and tablets to class? The class will be divided into two teams. One team will argue in favor of the topic and the other team will argue against it.

2. After several weeks of preparation, the day for the debate arrived. Jeff will represent the group arguing in favor, Jennifer will represent the group arguing against.

3. Here are their opening statements.
   Jeff: "We think allowing students to use their smartphones or tablets for school work in class is a good idea, because that will give them more opportunities to work independently at their own speeds or as a team, with fulltime access to computer-based capabilities, and give their teachers more time to give individual help. Having a smartphone in their possession will also allow students to participate in authorized extracurricular activities such as taking photos of school events or interviewing other students or faculty for the school newspaper."

4. Jennifer: "We think allowing students to bring their smartphones and tablets for school work in class is not a good idea. We favor the greater control that using school computers provides even though we do sacrifice some efficiency. Also, students have the option of finishing assignments at home on their smartphones or tablets."

5. Here are their statements supporting their positions and commenting on the other team's responses.
   Jeff: "Our teachers will usually explain all the details about an assignment to the entire class at the same

time. After that, students will be working independently at different speeds and will complete their assignment at different times. Those students who complete the assignment early can then quietly access another assignment online without having to interrupt the teacher or distract other students. This is especially important when different assignments are given to different students at the same time. Also, we eliminate the problem of students sitting idle waiting for a computer to become available, because, as you know, the school has not purchased enough computers to allow simultaneous access for an entire class."

6. "For team assignments, there is software available that allows team members to collaborate online, so each team member can see exactly what the other team members have entered into the common file, or can enter information himself/herself into the common file."

7. "If we handle assignments this way, the teacher will have more free time to help students who have questions. Best of all, the teacher can access online each student's progress with the assignment, either when she is in class, or after class, or after school, from inside or outside the school. And, if a student is absent, the teacher can quickly send homework assignments electronically to the student, eliminating the time spent arranging of a parent or another student to pick up and deliver the assignment."

8. Jennifer: "Allowing each student to use his/her smartphone or tablet in the classroom gives away too much freedom with too little oversight. There are students who will not handle that freedom well; bright students may complete the assignment quickly, and struggling students may become discouraged; in either case, they will have the means to access games or social media such as Facebook or Twitter and either waste class time by not moving on to another assignment or not give the necessary attention to their assignment. And what are you going to have the school do – install spyware that tracks what each student is doing on the computer, which then turns the teacher into a spy and enforcer and not a teacher?

9. It is easier for a teacher to monitor each student's work by walking around glancing at the screens of the school's computer system than trying to see what is displayed on the smaller screens on a smartphone or tablet."

10. "We are not against a student using his/her smartphone or tablet to complete work at home or to receive homework assignments if absent. We are also in favor of having software that allows the student to transmit work done on a smartphone or tablet at home to the school's computer system. We just don't like the idea of a student using these personal tools in the classroom; we prefer that students use the school computer system when at school."

11. "There are enough school computers for most students, but for those who have to wait, a teacher can assign other non-computer related tasks. Also, each student has a study period during which he/she can use a school computer. And, a teacher can access each student's work online from within the school or from a computer at home."

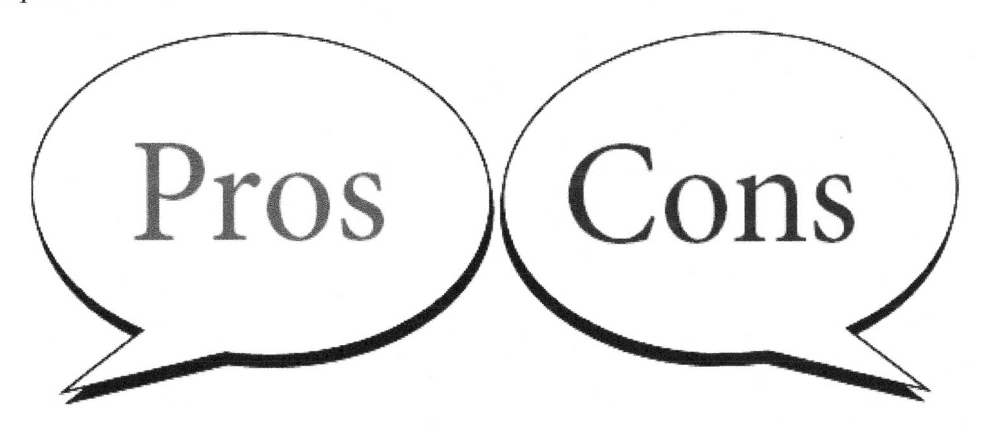

12. Here are their closing statements.
    Jeff: "In summary, greater flexibility and greater efficiency for students and teachers will result if students can use their smartphones and tablets for school work at school with access to the system from locations outside of the school."

13. Jennifer: "Requiring students to use the school computer system at school while allowing access to the school system from outside the school, will give them all the flexibility they need, while allowing teachers to do the necessary supervision and control over their students' work in school.

Corrections and Comments

Student Name:	**Date:**
Example: Essay introduces the topic clearly → "… teacher announced plans for a debate within her class. The topic will be: Should students be allowed to bring their smartphones and tablets to class?"	

Edited Version: Smartphones and Tablets in the Classroom
by George Smith and Vibhu Krishnaswamy

ESSAY	COMMENTS
Mrs. MacGregor, fifth grade English teacher, announced plans for a debate within her class. The topic will be: Should students be allowed to bring their smartphones and tablets to class? The class will be divided into two teams. One team will argue in favor of the topic and the other team will argue against it. After several weeks of preparation, the day for the debate arrived. Jeff will represent the group arguing in favor, Jennifer will represent the group arguing against.	**1. This essay introduces the topic clearly.** "… teacher announced plans for a debate within her class. The topic will be: Should students be allowed to bring their smartphones and tablets to class?" *CCSS.ELA-Literacy.W.5.1.a*
Here are their opening statements. Jeff: "We think allowing students to use their smartphones or tablets for school work in class is a good idea, because that will give them more opportunities to work independently at their own speeds or as a team, with fulltime access to computer-based capabilities, and give their teachers more time to give individual help. Having a smartphone in their possession will also allow students to participate in authorized extracurricular activities such as taking photos of school events or interviewing other students or faculty for the school newspaper." Jennifer: "We think allowing students to bring their smartphones and tablets for school work in class is	**2. The arguments of both teams are logically grouped and clearly stated.** In the opening statements group, in their statements supporting their positions and commenting on the other team's responses group, and in their closing statements group. *CCSS.ELA-Literacy.W.5.1.a* **3. Logically ordered reasons.** Within the two groups, the reasons are given in a logical manner. The reasons do not have to be in a specific order with each group. *CCSS.ELA-Literacy.W.5.1.b*

ESSAY	COMMENTS
not a good idea. We favor the greater control that using school computers provides even though we do sacrifice some efficiency. Also, students have the option of finishing assignments at home on their smartphones or tablets."	
Here are their statements supporting their positions and commenting on the other team's responses. Jeff: "Our teachers will usually explain all the details about an assignment to the entire class at the same time. After that, students will be working independently at different speeds and will complete their assignment at different times. Those students who complete the assignment early can then quietly access another assignment online without having to interrupt the teacher or distract other students. This is especially important when different assignments are given to different students at the same time. Also, we eliminate the problem of students sitting idle waiting for a computer to become available, because, as you know, the school has not purchased enough computers to allow simultaneous access for an entire class." "For team assignments, there is software available that allows team members to collaborate online, so each team member can see exactly what the other team members have entered into the common file, or can enter information himself/herself into the common file."	**4. Words, phrases and clauses that link arguments with supporting reasons and/or provide transitions.** Time transition: "after several weeks…" Cause transition: "is a good idea, because…" Addition transition: "Also, students have the option…" Contrast transition: "…even though we do sacrifice…" Summary transition: "In summary, greater flexibility…" *CCSS.ELA-Literacy.W.5.1.c*

ESSAY	COMMENTS
"If we handle assignments this way, the teacher will have more free time to help students who have questions. Best of all, the teacher can access online each student's progress with the assignment, either when she is in class, or after class, or after school, from inside or outside the school. And, if a student is absent, the teacher can quickly send homework assignments electronically to the student, eliminating the time spent arranging of a parent or another student to pick up and deliver the assignment." Jennifer: "Allowing each student to use his/her smartphone or tablet in the classroom gives away too much freedom with too little oversight. There are students who will not handle that freedom well; bright students may complete the assignment quickly, and struggling students may become discouraged; in either case, they will have the means to access games or social media such as Facebook or Twitter and either waste class time by not moving on to another assignment or not give the necessary attention to their assignment. And what are you going to have the school do – install spyware that tracks what each student is doing on the computer, which then turns the teacher into a spy and enforcer and not a teacher? It is easier for a teacher to monitor each student's work by walking around glancing at the screens of the school's computer system than trying to see what is displayed on the smaller screens on a smartphone or tablet."	

ESSAY	COMMENTS
"We are not against a student using his/her smartphone or tablet to complete work at home or to receive homework assignments if absent. We are also in favor of having software that allows the student to transmit work done on a smartphone or tablet at home to the school's computer system. We just don't like the idea of a student using these personal tools in the classroom; we prefer that students use the school computer system when at school."	
"There are enough school computers for most students, but for those who have to wait, a teacher can assign other non-computer related tasks. Also, each student has a study period during which he/she can use a school computer. And, a teacher can access each student's work online from within the school or from a computer at home."	
Here are their closing statements. Jeff: "In summary, greater flexibility and greater efficiency for students and teachers will result if students can use their smartphones and tablets for school work at school with access to the system from locations outside of the school."	**5. Concluding statement:** Each team spokesperson makes a concluding statement. *CCSS.ELA-Literacy.W.5.1.d*
Jennifer: "Requiring students to use the school computer system at school while allowing access to the school system from outside the school, will give them all the flexibility they need, while allowing teachers to do the necessary supervision and control over their students' work in school.	

Your Suggested Topics:

Exercises Ideas:

1. Why you need a helmet when riding your bike
2. Why you should elect me class president
3. Why every team member should get playing time
4. Why gym, art and music classes are important
5. Why I should receive an allowance

Text Types and Purposes Category: Informative

Standard: CCSS.ELA-Literacy.W.5.2

Informative: Serving to inform or educate or instruct by giving information about a topic.

- You normally write informative essays or stories in the first or third person.

Title: Butterflies by Jasmine Brunton

1. There are many different types of butterflies in the world. Butterflies are found in most places around the world. In the following we will explore different types of butterflies and where they can be found around the globe. We will explore to see if there are any that are endangered, or even poisonous.

2. There are many different types of butterflies around the world. The most famous one is the Monarch Butterfly. The Monarch butterfly can be found mostly in North and South America, but you can also find them as far away as Australia. The Monarch Butterfly can fly as fast as 25 miles per hour during their migration from Mexico to their destination in North America. There is two different species of Monarch Butterfly one that can be found in North America and the other is the South American species. Both of them come from the Caribbean but Migrate to their final destinations in either North or South America. (Monarch butterfly.com)

3. One of the many butterflies that are endangered in the United States is the Bay Checkerspot Butterfly. This Butterfly is considered threatened in the United States. They are considered to be a medium sized butterfly, and only have a 2 inch wing span. This butterfly is endangered because they are losing their habitat as a result of Air pollution among other things. The majority of these butterflies can be found in California. (www.FWS.gov)

4. There are no butterflies that are poisonous to humans, but there are some that are birds will only eat once because they taste so bad. These butterflies are like this because when they are caterpillars they eat poisonous plants like milkweed. When they become butterflies it makes them taste bad to birds and other animals.

5. Butterflies are numerous around the world. There are many different varieties all around the world. From the Monarch to the Checkerspot butterfly they come in many different sizes. There are some that are bad tasting to birds but none that are poisonous to humans. The butterfly is something you can find where ever you go around the world.

Corrections and Comments

Student Name:	**Date:**
Example: Line #1 →There are many different ~~types~~ **species** of butterflies in the world.	

Edited Version: Butterflies by Jasmine Brunton

ESSAY

There are many different ~~types~~ [**species**] of butterflies in the world. Butterflies are found in most places around the world. In ~~the following~~ [***this essay,***] we will explore different ~~types~~ [***species***] of butterflies and where they can be found ~~around the globe. We will explore to see if there are~~ [***and whether***] any ~~that~~ are endangered, or even poisonous.

~~There are many different types species of butterflies around the world.~~ The most famous [***species***] ~~one~~ is the Monarch butterfly. Monarch butterfl~~y~~ [***ies***] can be found mostly in North and South America, but ~~you can~~ also ~~find them~~ as far away as Australia. ~~The~~ Monarch butterfl~~y~~ [***ies***] can fly as fast as 25 miles per hour during their migration from Mexico to their destination in North America. There ~~is~~ [***are***] two different species of Monarch Butterfly: one that can be found in North America and the other ~~is the~~ [***in***] South America~~n species~~. Both of them come from the Caribbean but migrate to their final destinations in either North or South America. ([***For more information, visit***] Monarch butterfly.com)

COMMENTS

1. This essay introduces a topic clearly and provides facts and concrete details.

"There are many different species of butterflies in the world. Butterflies are found in most places around the world. In this essay, we will explore different species of butterflies and where they can be found and whether any are endangered, or even poisonous."

"The Monarch Butterfly can fly as fast as 25 miles per hour…"

2. This essay provides a general observation.

"There are many different species of butterflies in the world. Butterflies are found in most places around the world."

3. There is a narrator who tells the story in the third person (a story written in the third person uses the pronouns "he, she."). The author does not put herself in the actual story.

CCSS ELA-Literacy.W.5.2.a and CCSS ELA-Literacy.W.5.2.b

ESSAY	COMMENTS
One of the ~~many butterflies~~ butterfly species that ~~are~~ [*is*] endangered in the United States is the Bay Checkerspot butterfly. ~~This Butterfly is considered threatened in the United States. They are~~ [***It is***] considered ~~to be~~ a medium sized butterfly, ~~and only have~~ [***with***] a 2 inch wing span. This butterfly is endangered because ~~they are~~ [***it is***] losing ~~their~~ [***its***] habitat as a result of air pollution among other things. The majority of these butterflies can be found in California. (www.FWS.gov)	**4. Transitional words and phrases - links between ideas.** *Place transition:* "…come *from* the Caribbean but migrate *to* their final destinations…." *Cause transition:* "…*because* when they are caterpillars they eat poisonous plants like milkweed." *Time transition:* "…because *when* they are caterpillars they eat poisonous plants like milkweed." *CCSS ELA-Literacy.W.5.2.c*
There are no butterflies that are poisonous to humans, but there are some that ~~are~~ birds will only eat once because they taste so bad. These butterflies are like this because when they are caterpillars they eat poisonous plants like milkweed. When they become butterflies it makes them taste bad to birds and other animals.	**5. Precise language and domain-specific vocabulary.** **5.1** Lack of agreement between a singular noun and a plural pronoun: "The Monarch ***butterfly***… during ***their*** migration …." "Butterfly" is singular while "their" is plural. Change it either to "butterflies" and "their" or "butterfly" and "its." *CCSS ELA-Literacy.L.5.1*
Butterflies are numerous around the world [***with***] ~~There are~~ many different varieties ~~all around the world~~. From the Monarch to the Checkerspot butterfly they come in many different sizes. There are some that are bad tasting to birds but none that are poisonous to humans. The butterfly is something you can find wherever you go around the world.	**6. Conclusion:** "Butterflies are numerous around the world with many different varieties From the Monarch to the Checkerspot butterfly they come in many different sizes. There are some that are bad tasting to birds but none that are poisonous to humans. The butterfly is something you can find wherever you go around the world." *CCSS ELA-Literacy.W.5.2.e*

ESSAY	COMMENTS
	7. References to information: **7.1** The author includes a reference to the website www.FWS.gov (government fish and wildlife site). It would be helpful to the reader if she gave more detail about where the information is on that website that she wants the reader to see. Assuming it had to do with butterflies, butterflies were not displayed on the home page. Or, the author mentioned this site in order to give credit for information she used from the site. If she copied information from the website and used it in this essay, she has to place a footnote at the end of the information she copied. **7.2** The author also includes a reference to www.Monarchbutterfly.com. If she copied information from the website and used it in this essay, she has to place a footnote at the end of the information she copied. If she just included it for readers who want more information, she should have added: "***For more information, visit…***"

Title: Lewis E. Waterman by Emily Adams

1. Lewis E. Waterman was an American inventor and an insurance salesman who developed a relatively leak-proof fountain pen in 1884.

2. Before his fountain pen, pen tips had to be dipped into ink after every few words. Waterman was also the first person to place a clip on the cap.

3. It is important because, if we didn't have these pens, then we would have a messy classroom that had leaks everywhere. We wouldn't have nice clean pens to write with, we would also spill a lot of ink all the time.

4. I think that Lewis Waterman is a great inventor.

Corrections and Comments

Student Name:	**Date:**
Example: Sentence #2 → Before ***he invented*** his fountain pen, pen tips had to be dipped into ink after every few words.	

Edited Version: Lewis E. Waterman by Emily Adams

ESSAY	COMMENTS
Lewis E. Waterman was an American inventor and an insurance salesman who developed a relatively leak-proof fountain pen in 1884.	**1. This essay introduces a topic clearly and provides facts and concrete details.** "Lewis E. Waterman was an American inventor and an insurance salesman who developed a relatively leak-proof fountain pen in 1884." "Waterman was also the first person to place a clip on the cap."
Before [***he invented***] his fountain pen, pen tips had to be dipped into ink after every few words. Waterman was also the first person to place a clip on the cap.	**2. This essay provides a general observation.** "Before his fountain pen, pen tips had to be dipped into ink after every few words." **3. There is a narrator** who tells the story in the third person (a story written in the third person uses the pronouns "he, she."). The author does not put herself in the actual story. *CCSS ELA-Literacy.W.5.2.a and CCSS ELA-Literacy.W.5.2.b* **4. Transitional words and phrases – links between ideas.** *Time transition: "Before* his fountain pen…"; "the *first* person to place a clip…" *Contrast transition: "…if* we didn't have these pens, *then* we would have…" *CCSS ELA-Literacy.W.5.2.c*

ESSAY	COMMENTS
	5. Precise language and domain-specific vocabulary. "…was an American inventor…"; "…a relatively leak-proof fountain pen…"; "…pen tips had to be dipped into ink after every few words."; "a clip on the cap." *CCSS ELA-Literacy.W.5.2.d*
It is important because, if we didn't have these pens, then we would have a messy classroom that had ~~leaks~~ [***ink stains from leaky pens***] everywhere. We wouldn't have nice clean pens to write with. ~~we would also spill a lot of ink all the time.~~ *[Editor's note: The last phrase is not necessary; the first sentence in this paragraph says the same thing.]*	**6. Conclusion:** "…if we didn't have these pens, then we would have a messy classroom that had ink stains from leaky pens everywhere. We wouldn't have nice clean pens to write with. "I think that Lewis Waterman is a great inventor." *CCSS ELA-Literacy.W.5.2.e*
I think that Lewis Waterman is a great inventor.	
	7. Incomplete information: **7.1** The author could have added more detail about how Waterman's pen was better than any pen invented before it and why the clip he developed was useful. Examples: "…who developed a relatively leak-proof fountain pen in 1884. Before his fountain pen, pen tips had to be dipped into ink after every few words *and the flow of ink was not controlled, so too much ink frequently flowed from the tip onto the paper,*

ESSAY	COMMENTS
	creating ink stains. Waterman's pen used a scientific principle called "capillarity," which recognizes that there is attraction and repulsion between a liquid (ink) and a solid (the pen tube). Also, his pen allowed air to enter the pen tube, and the combination of capillarity and air created a steady flow of ink to the tip. The pen also stored ink so that more words could be written between refills." **7.2** "Waterman was also the first person to place a clip on the cap. *The clip allowed the pen to be attached securely to the writer's pocket, a convenient location for the writer to reach it."*

Title: Nick Allen by Emily Adams

1. Hi. I'm Emily, reporter for the Great Mountain Middle School newspaper. A friend of mine at another middle school told me a true story about a prankster in her class who got himself in trouble.

2. I decided to write an article about him for my school newspaper because I thought his story taught a lesson about behavior that some of my classmates could learn from. Here is my article (I used a fictitious name for him to protect his reputation).

Nick Allen

3. Nick Allen was one of a kind. His friends thought he was smart and fun to be around, and that he definitely had a sense of humor – or was it mischief – that made him popular. Was he a prankster or a troublemaker? I'll let you decide.

4. One time after his third grade teacher finished teaching about the ocean, Nick thought it would be fun to turn his classroom into a beach. With help from his older brother who could drive, he delivered two bags of sand, two beach chairs, an umbrella and two beach balls to his classroom after school. Unfortunately for him, the janitor caught him before he could finish setting up the room.
   Punishment: For three days he had to stay in school during recess and stay after school to write an essay about the ocean

5. In 4th grade he noticed that his teacher had a nose like a hawk's beak. Thinking about the nose prompted him to do some research on birds, where he read about a blackbird that confused hunters with its peep because they could not tell where it was coming from.

6. He, in class the next day, made the same peep noises, and after awhile his teacher blamed 2 different students. They denied doing this, but some other students began doing it too.

7. The teacher confronted all the suspects (he did not suspect Mick) and threatened severe punishments if they did not tell who started this prank, and one of them fingered Nick. Punishment: Nick was forced to join a local birdwatching hike which lasted 3 hours, and to write a long report about the birds he saw on the hike.

8. Then Nick graduated to fifth grade. He did not like going to art class; he just did not enjoy doing art projects. He noticed that the art teacher was at lunch the same time he was, and that they were the next class after lunch to take art. One day, he hid a rubber snake in his backpack and during lunch hour, snuck into the art classroom and hid the rubber snake in the container where the paints were stored.

9. Shortly after class started, the teacher told the students to get their supplies; loud screams interrupted the class as students scrambled to get away from the paint cabinet. The teacher had to take most of the class time calming everyone down.
   Unfortunately for Nick, another teacher remembered seeing him coming out of the art classroom during lunch hour.

10. The principal decided that three pranks were enough and that he was going to make an example out of Nick. At the spring carnival he volunteered Nick to be in the dunking booth, where students happily lined up to throw a ball and hit a target that tipped his seat and dropped him into the water. Then Nick had to sit in the face painting booth to have **his face** painted over and over again by whomever came there. He was also told that if he did any more pranks, he would be suspended and not graduate.

11. So let me ask you: Were the pranks worth the punishments? Think about that the next time you think about playing a prank in our school.

Corrections and Comments

Student Name:	Date:
Example: **Essay introduces a topic clearly** → A friend of mine at another middle school told me a true story about a prankster…	

Edited Version: Nick Allen by Emily Adams

ESSAY	COMMENTS
Hi. I'm Emily, reporter for the Great Mountain Middle School newspaper. A friend of mine at another middle school told me a true story about a prankster in her class who got himself in trouble.	**1. This essay introduces a topic clearly and provides facts and concrete details and precise language.** **1.1** "A friend of mine at another middle school told me a true story about a prankster…."
I decided to write an article about him for my school newspaper because I thought his story taught a lesson about behavior that some of my classmates could learn from. Here is my article (I used a fictitious name for him to protect his reputation).	**1.2** "I decided to write an article about him for my school newspaper…." **1.3** "Nick Allen was one of a kind." **1.4** "Was he a prankster or a troublemaker?" **1.5** "...to turn his classroom into a beach." **1.6** "...he delivered two bags of sand, two beach chairs, an umbrella and two beach balls…"
Nick Allen Nick Allen was one of a kind. His friends thought he was smart and fun to be around, and that he definitely had a sense of humor – or was it mischief – that made him popular. Was he a prankster or a troublemaker? I'll let you decide.	**1.7** "He, in class the next day, made the same peep noises…" **2. This essay provides a general observation.** **2.1** "I decided to write an article about him for my school newspaper because I thought his story taught a lesson about behavior that some of my classmates could learn from."
One time after his third grade teacher finished teaching about the ocean, Nick thought it would be fun to turn his classroom into a beach. With help from his older brother who could drive, he delivered two bags of sand, two beach chairs, an umbrella and two beach balls to his classroom after school. Unfortunately for him, the janitor caught him before he could finish setting up the room. Punishment: For three days he had to stay in school during recess and stay after school to write an essay about the ocean	**2.2** "…were the pranks worth the punishments? Think about that the next time you think about playing a prank in our school."

ESSAY	COMMENTS
In 4th grade he noticed that his teacher had a nose like a hawk's beak. Thinking about the nose prompted him to do some research on birds, where he read about a blackbird that confused hunters with its peep because they could not tell where it was coming from.	**3. This essay groups information logically.** **3.1** The character Nick is described and introduced first. **3.2** Next, his pranks are described in sequential order by grade (3rd then 4th then 5th). **3.3** Last, the author makes a conclusion.
~~He, in class the next day,~~ [***In class the next day, he***] made the same peep noises, and after awhile his teacher blamed 2 different students. They denied doing this, but some other students began doing it too. The teacher confronted all the suspects (he did not suspect Mick) and threatened severe punishments if they did not tell who started this prank, and one of them fingered Nick. Punishment: Nick was forced to join a local birdwatching hike which lasted 3 hours, and to write a long report about the birds he saw on the hike.	**4. There is a narrator** who tells the story in both the first and third persons. The author introduces herself in the beginning of the essay in the first person, using the pronouns "I" and "me." But the article itself is written in the third person using the pronouns "he" and "his" to describe Nick. *CCSS ELA-Literacy.W.5.2.a and* *CCSS ELA-Literacy.W.5.2.b and* *CCSS ELA-Literacy.W.5.2.d*
Then Nick graduated to fifth grade. He did not like going to art class; he just did not enjoy doing art projects. He noticed that the art teacher was at lunch the same time he was, and that they were the next class after lunch to take art. One day, he hid a rubber snake in his backpack and during lunch hour, snuck into the art classroom and hid the rubber snake in the container where the paints were stored.	**5. Transitional words and phrases – links between ideas.** *Time transition:* "One time *after* his third grade teacher…"; "He, in class the *next* day…"; "Shortly *after* class started…"; "*Then* Nick graduated to fifth grade." *Cause transition:* "…*because* I thought his story taught a lesson…" *Effect transition:* "*Unfortunately* for him…" *CCSS ELA-Literacy.W.5.2.c*

ESSAY	COMMENTS
Shortly after class started, the teacher told the students to get their supplies; loud screams interrupted the class as students scrambled to get away from the paint cabinet. The teacher had to take most of the class time calming everyone down. Unfortunately for Nick, another teacher remembered seeing him coming out of the art classroom during lunch hour. The principal decided that three pranks were enough and that he was going to make an example out of Nick. At the spring carnival he volunteered Nick to be in the dunking booth, where students happily lined up to throw a ball and hit a target that tipped his seat and dropped him into the water. Then Nick had to sit in the face painting booth to have **his face** painted over and over again by whomever came there. He was also told that if he did any more pranks, he would be suspended and not graduate.	
So let me ask you: Were the pranks worth the punishments? Think about that the next time you think about playing a prank in our school.	**6. Conclusion.** "So let me ask you: were the pranks worth the punishments? Think about that the next time you think about playing a prank in our school." *CCSS ELA-Literacy.W.5.2.e*

ESSAY	COMMENTS
	7. Inconsistent number format. Sometimes a quantity is expressed as a figure (2, 3), sometimes as a word (third, fifth) and sometimes as a combination (4th). The author should choose one of these formats to use for all quantities. **8. Bonding author and reader.** *In this essay, the author involves the reader by asking questions:* "Was he a prankster or a troublemaker? I'll let you decide." "So let me ask you: were the pranks worth the punishments?" *The author also asks the reader to take action:* "Think about that…"

Your Suggested Topics:

Exercises Ideas:

1. Biographical facts about my favorite (actor, singer, athlete etc.)
2. What is it like to be an (actor, singer, athlete etc.)?
3. Rules for bicycle riders
4. How Facebook was invented
5. Information about our (community service, dance, art etc.) club

Text Types and Purposes Category: Explanatory

Standard: CCSS.ELA-Literacy.W.5.2

Explanatory: Serving to explain or clarify by giving information about a topic.

- Explain how to perform or accomplish a process or task or procedure or how to resolve a problem or overcome an obstacle.
- You normally write explanatory essays or stories in the second person.

Title: Blowing Bubbles by Emily Adams

1. Do you want to learn how to blow a bubble? Well, let me show you.

2. First of all you put bubble gum in your mouth and chew it (don't swallow it!).

3. The next step is to put your tongue under the gum and move the gum to the top of your mouth. With the gum now sandwiched between the top of your tongue and the top of your mouth, make the gum flat by pressing your tongue against it. After that, wrap the gum around your tongue. Then make the gum thin and begin to blow it out slowly. A bubble will begin to form. Keep blowing out air through your mouth and into the bubble to make the bubble larger, but make sure the bubble isn't too big or it will pop!

4. There is no dought that following these steps will allow you blow a bubble!

Corrections and Comments

Student Name:	Date:
Example: Line #2 → First ~~of all you~~ put bubble gum in your mouth and chew it (don't swallow it!).	

Edited Version: Blowing Bubbles by Emily Adams

ESSAY	COMMENTS
Do you want to learn how to blow a bubble? Well, let me show you.	**1. This essay introduces the topic clearly.** 1.1 "Do you want to learn how to blow a bubble? Well, let me show you." 1.2 This essay is written in the second person point of view, which means the author is directing the information to you, the reader. This point of view uses the pronouns "you" or "yours." *CCSS.ELA-Literacy.W.5.2.a*
First ~~of all you~~ put bubble gum in your mouth and chew it (don't swallow it!). ~~The next step is to~~ [***Second,***] put your tongue under the gum and move the gum to the top of your mouth. [***Third,***] ~~W~~ [***w***]ith the gum now sandwiched between the top of your tongue and the top of your mouth, make the gum flat by pressing your tongue against it. ~~After that~~ [***Fourth***], wrap the gum around your tongue.	**2. Develop the topic with facts, concrete details, examples, precise language and domain-specific vocabulary.** **2.1** This essay uses precise language to describe every step in the procedure to blow a bubble. Examples: "…put your tongue under the gum and move the gum to the top of your mouth."; "…make the gum flat by pressing your tongue against it." **2.2** Domain-specific vocabulary is used. "tongue"; "gum"; "bubble" *CCSS.ELA-Literacy.W.5.2.b and CCSS.ELA-Literacy.W.5.2.d*
~~Then~~ [***Fifth,***] make the gum thin and begin to blow it out slowly. A bubble will begin to form. [***Last,***] ~~K~~ [***k***]eep blowing out air through your mouth and into the bubble to make the bubble larger, but make sure the bubble isn't too big or it will pop!	**3. Words, phrases and clauses that link ideas within and across categories of information.** *Addition transitions: "first"; "next"; "then"* *CCSS.ELA-Literacy.W.5.2.c*

ESSAY	COMMENTS
There is no ~~dought~~ [***doubt***] that following these steps will allow you blow a bubble!	**4. Concluding statement.** "There is no doubt that following these steps will allow you blow a bubble!" *CCSS.ELA-Literacy.W.5.2.e* **5. Choice of words.** **5.1.** *Author choice:* "Well, let me *show* you." *Suggested choice:* "Well, let me *tell* you." Show is better if graphics such as pictures were used in the essay, but since only word descriptions are used, tell is a better choice. **5.2** *Author choice:* "After that, wrap the gum around your tongue." *Suggested choice:* "After that, wrap the gum around your tongue *like a hotdog in a roll.*" Adding the simile "*like a hotdog in a roll*" makes the instruction more interesting to the description and makes the instruction absolutely clear. **6. Missing information:** *Author choice:* "Then make the gum thin and begin to blow it out slowly." *Correction:* The author needs to give a more detailed description about how to make the gum thin, and more detail about how to position the gum on the tongue so that when you blow air through your mouth, the air goes into the gum and makes it expand into a bubble.

Title: How To Make Homemade Chocolate Chip Cookies
by Jasmine Brunton

1. Everyone loves Chocolate Chip Cookies! Did you know that you can make them homemade? They are even better than the ones that you buy in the store! All you need to do is gather up the needed ingredients to make them all by yourself, or with your parents. You're going to love how easy it is to make Chocolate Chip Cookies with this easy recipe explained.

2. The First thing you need to do is gather up the needed ingredients. You will need 1 1/2 cups of all-purpose flour. Next thing you will need is 3/4 tsp. baking soda. After that you will need ½ tsp. baking powder. You will also need ½ tsp. salt and 2/3 cup granulated sugar. Next you will need 2/3 cup firmly packed dark brown sugar and 1 egg. Once you gather that you will need 1 ½ tsp. vanilla extract, and finally you will need 2 cups of both semi-sweet chocolate chips and white chocolate chips.

3. Once you gather all the ingredients, you will need to preheat the oven to 375, and grease the cookie sheet. Next you have to combine flour, baking soda, baking powder, and salt in a medium bowl set to the side till later. Then you will need to mix the butter with sugars together in a large bowl it is recommended that you use an electric mixer. You should mix this till it is light and fluffy. This should take about 5 minutes to complete.

4. Next mix in the egg and Vanilla and continue to mix until it is complete mixed in. You will now need to retrieve the medium bowl that you mixed together earlier, and dump it into the large bowl. Once it has been dumped into the bowl you will need to mix this together thoroughly. Finally add the white and chocolate chips to the mixture, and stir until completely mixed in.

5. Once this is complete you will drop tablespoons full of cookie dough mix onto a cookie sheet leaving a 2 inch space between each dropping. You will then need to put the cookie sheets into the oven. Ask your parents to put the cookie sheets into the oven, it will be hot and you will not want to burn yourself. Bake

for 10 minutes or until golden brown. Once done have your parents take the cookie sheets out of the oven, and let cool for 5 to 10 minutes. Once cooled, enjoy and share with your friends and family!

6. Cookies are fun and easy to make even as a project for you and your family! The cookies you make are even better than the ones you buy in the store. Instead of buying cookies, follow this recipe to help you make delicious cookies everyone will love! It's so easy to do!

Corrections and Comments

Student Name:	**Date:**
Example: Line #1 → Everyone loves Chocolate Chip Cookies! Did you know that ~~you can make them~~	
they can be homemade?	

Edited Version: How To Make Homemade Chocolate Chip Cookies
by Jasmine Brunton

ESSAY	COMMENTS
Everyone loves Chocolate Chip Cookies! Did you know that ~~you can make them~~ [***they can be***] homemade? They are even better than the ones that you buy in the store! All you need to do is gather up the needed ingredients [***and follow a recipe, like this one,***] to make them all by yourself, or with your parents. You're going to love how easy it is to make Chocolate Chip Cookies with this easy recipe. ~~explained.~~ *[Editor's note: It is not necessary to capitalize Chocolate Chip Cookies unless it is a brand name. But there is no harm in doing it if the author wants the phrase to stand out.]*	**1. This essay introduces the topic clearly.** **1.1** "You're going to love how easy it is to make Chocolate Chip Cookies with this easy recipe." **1.2** This essay is written in the second person point of view, which means the author is directing the information to you, the reader. This point of view uses the pronouns "you" or "yours." *CCSS.ELA-Literacy.W.5.2.a*
The ~~F~~ [f]irst thing you need to do is gather up the ~~needed~~ ingredients. You will need 1 1/2 cups of all-purpose flour[,] ~~Next thing you will need is~~ 3/4 tsp. baking soda[,] ~~After that you will need~~ ½ tsp. baking powder[,] ~~You will also need~~ ½ tsp. salt and 2/3 cup granulated sugar. Next you will need 2/3 cup firmly packed dark brown sugar and 1 egg. Once you gather ~~that~~ [***those items***] you will need 1 ½ tsp. vanilla extract, and ~~finally you will need~~ 2 cups of both semi-sweet chocolate chips and white chocolate chips. [*Editor's note: the author should choose one format for fractions, either 1/2 or ½.*]	**2. Develop the topic with facts, concrete details, examples, precise language and domain-specific vocabulary.** **2.1** The recipe instructions give facts and concrete details such as what to do in each step and precise measurements of each ingredient. **2.2** Domain-specific vocabulary is used. "cup," "tsp," "degrees," "mix," "preheat," "bake." *CCSS.ELA-Literacy.W.5.2.b and CCSS.ELA-Literacy.W.5.2.d*

ESSAY	COMMENTS
Once you gather all the ingredients, ~~you will need to~~ preheat the oven to 375, [*Editor's note: express this either as 375^0 or 375 degrees.*] and grease the cookie sheet. Next ~~you have to~~ combine flour, baking soda, baking powder, and salt in a medium bowl [***and***] set [***it***] to the side till later. Then ~~you will need to~~ mix the butter with sugars together in a large bowl, ~~it is recommended that you use~~ [***preferably using***] an electric mixer, ~~You should mix this~~ [***un***]til it is light and fluffy. This should take about 5 minutes to complete. Once this is complete you will drop tablespoons full of cookie dough mix onto a cookie sheet leaving a 2 inch space between each dropping. ~~You will then need to~~ [***Then***] put the cookie sheets into the oven. ~~Ask your parents to put the cookie sheets into the oven, it will be hot and you will not want to burn yourself.~~ [*Editor's note: I don't think the cookie sheets are hot yet; they won't be hot until they come out of the oven, so anyone can pick them up and put them in the oven.*] Bake for 10 minutes or until golden brown. Once done have your parents take the cookie sheets out of the oven [***(because they will be hot)***], and let cool for 5 to 10 minutes. Once cooled, enjoy and share with your friends and family!	**3. Words, phrases and clauses that link ideas within and across categories of information.** *Addition transitions:* "The *first* thing you need…"; "*Next* you will need…"; *Time transitions:* "*Next* you will need…"; "*Once* you gather…"; "*Then* you will need…" *CCSS.ELA-Literacy.W.5.2.c*

ESSAY	COMMENTS
Cookies are fun and easy to make even as a project for you and your family! The cookies you make are even better than the ones you buy in the store. Instead of buying cookies, follow this recipe to help you make delicious cookies everyone will love! It's so easy to do!	**4. Concluding statement.** "Instead of buying cookies, follow this recipe to help you make delicious cookies everyone will love! It's so easy to do!" *CCSS.ELA-Literacy.W.5.2.e* **5. Choice of format.** **5.1.** The format the author used to describe the recipe is OK, although there are too many unnecessary words and too many sentences. The editor has lined out the unnecessary words and combined the instructions into fewer sentences. **5.2** There is another choice of format for the recipe: a list in which each instruction is numbered as a separate step. A list would make a neater appearance and would probably be easier to read because there are more unnecessary words that could be deleted.

Title: How Aircraft Fly by George Smith

1. At your age, you must have heard the term "gravity" and may have an idea of how it works. Gravity is a force that pulls downward toward the center of the earth and acts on objects that are on the ground, in the water or in the air. It is gravity that makes you come back down to earth when you jump up in the air.

2. If gravity has this effect on your body, you can imagine the effect it has on a jet airplane, which weighs much more than you do. You may have wondered how something as heavy as a jet airplane can rise in the air against the force of gravity pulling it down. You probably think the answer is because of its powerful engines.

3. But let me ask you: how would you explain why gliders without engines can still fly? Or how would you explain the fact that if someone designed an airplane whose top and bottom wing surfaces were both flat, it would have a very difficult time gaining altitude, even with a powerful engine (you'll have to take my word on this that this would be true)?

4. The only explanation that answers these questions is the shape of the wing surfaces. The front of the **top** surface of the wing is thicker than the rear surface, so that the wing surface is curved. The front and back of the **bottom** surface of the wing is the same thickness – it is flat.

5. So how does the design of the wings allow the aircraft to gain altitude and fly? Here's how: As the aircraft picks up speed on takeoff, the air rushing over the top wing surface is slowed down by the thick front edge of the wing. The air rushing over the bottom surface is not slowed down because that surface is flat. Because the air under the wind is moving faster than the air over the wing, the air pressure across the bottom surface of the wing is greater than the air pressure across the top surface of the wing, and that air pressure pushes upward on the wing and the body of the aircraft, so the airplane rises. Yes, engines provide the speed for takeoff (gliders must be towed by a powered airplane), but it is the shape of the wing that provides the upward lift.

6. Now when you are at an airport watching a plane take off, you can explain to the people you are with how the design of the wing allows the aircraft to rise.

Corrections and Comments

Student Name:	Date:
Example: Topic is clear → "You may have wondered how something as heavy as a jet airplane can rise in the air against the force of gravity pulling it down."	

Edited Version: How Aircraft Fly by George Smith

ESSAY	COMMENTS
At your age, you must have heard the term "gravity" and may have an idea of how it works. Gravity is a force that pulls downward toward the center of the earth and acts on objects that are on the ground, in the water or in the air. It is gravity that makes you come back down to earth when you jump up in the air.	**1. This essay introduces the topic clearly.** **1.1** "You may have wondered how something as heavy as a jet airplane can rise in the air against the force of gravity pulling it down." **1.2** "So how does the design of the wings allow the aircraft to gain altitude and fly?"
If gravity has this effect on your body, you can imagine the effect it has on a jet airplane, which weighs much more than you do. You may have wondered how something as heavy as a jet airplane can rise in the air against the force of gravity pulling it down. You probably think the answer is because of its powerful engines.	**1.3** This essay is written in the second person point of view, which means the author is directing the information to you, the reader. This point of view uses the pronouns "you" or "yours." *CCSS.ELA-Literacy.W.5.2.a*
But let me ask you: how would you explain why gliders without engines can still fly? Or how would you explain the fact that if someone designed an airplane whose top and bottom wing surfaces were both flat, it would have a very difficult time gaining altitude, even with a powerful engine (you'll have to take my word on this that this would be true)?	**2. Develop the topic with facts, concrete details, examples, precise language and domain-specific vocabulary.** **2.1** "Gravity is a force that pulls downward toward the center of the earth and acts on objects that are on the ground, in the water, or in the air."
The only explanation that answers these questions is the shape of the wing surfaces. The front of the **top** surface of the wing is thicker than the rear surface, so that the wing surface is curved. The front and back of the **bottom** surface of the wing is the same thickness – it is flat.	**2.2** "The only explanation that answers these questions is the shape of the wing surfaces. The front of the **top** surface of the wing is thicker than the rear surface, so that the wing surface is curved. The front and back of the **bottom** surface of the wing is the same thickness – it is flat."

ESSAY	COMMENTS
So how does the design of the wings allow the aircraft to gain altitude and fly? Here's how: As the aircraft picks up speed on takeoff, the air rushing over the top wing surface is slowed down by the thick front edge of the wing. The air rushing over the bottom surface is not slowed down because that surface is flat. Because the air under the wind is moving faster than the air over the wing, the air pressure across the bottom surface of the wing is greater than the air pressure across the top surface of the wing, and that air pressure pushes upward on the wing and the body of the aircraft, so the airplane rises. Yes, engines provide the speed for takeoff (gliders must be towed by a powered airplane), but it is the shape of the wing that provides the upward lift.	**2.3** "As the aircraft picks up speed on takeoff, the air rushing over the top wing surface is slowed down by the thick front edge of the wing. The air rushing over the bottom surface is not slowed down because that surface is flat. Because the air under the wind is moving faster than the air over the wing, the air pressure across the bottom surface of the wing is greater than the air pressure across the top surface of the wing, and that air pressure pushes upward on the wing and the body of the aircraft, so the airplane rises." *CCSS.ELA-Literacy.W.5.2.b and CCSS.ELA-Literacy.W.5.2.d* **3. Words, phrases and clauses that link categories of information supporting reasons and/or provide transitions.** *Cause transitions:* "Because the air under the wind is moving faster…" *Clarification transition:* "The only explanation that answers these questions…" *Contrast transition:* "but it is the shape of the wing…" *CCSS.ELA-Literacy.W.5.2.c*

ESSAY	COMMENTS
Now when you are at an airport watching a plane take off, you can explain to the people you are with how the design of the wing allows the aircraft to rise.	**4. Concluding statement:** “Now when you are at an airport watching a plane take off, you can explain to the people you are with how the design of the wing allows the aircraft to rise.” *CCSS.ELA-Literacy.W.5.2.e*

Your Suggested Topics:

Exercises Ideas:

1. How to catch a fish
2. Why leaves change color
3. What caused ocean tides
4. How to plan for a camping trip
5. How food is digested

NOTES

NOTES